COINS OF ENGLAND

& THE UNITED KINGDOM

DECIMAL ISSUES
STANDARD CATALOGUE OF BRITISH COINS
PART 3

SPINK

LONDON

A Catalogue of the Decimal Coins of Great Britain
and Ireland

Standard Catalogue of British Coins
Coins of England and the United Kingdom
3rd edition, 2017

© Spink & Son Ltd, 2016
69 Southampton Row, Bloomsbury
London WC1B 4ET

Typeset by Design to Print UK Ltd,
9 & 10 Riverview Business Park, Forest Row, East Sussex RH18 5DW
www.designtoprintuk.com
Printed and bound in Malta by
Gutenberg Press Ltd.

ISBN 978-1-907427-99-2

CONTENTS

ACKNOWLEDGEMENTS

We wish to acknowledge the valuable contributions of the following who have submitted information and provided photographs which have greatly enhanced this edition.

Kevin Clancy, *Royal Mint*
Paul Davies
David Fletcher
Jenny Manders, *Royal Mint*

FOREWORD

Welcome to the third edition of the Coins of England Decimal Issues.

As the Royal Mint continues to issue new coins and offers each year, the Decimal Issues catalogue will become an important source of reference to collectors of coins from 1971. The aim of this separate catalogue is to provide the most comprehensive record of Mint issues and while we acknowledge the help with illustrations, sadly information regarding sales of coins and sets is still lacking to the detriment of collectors and dealers in these issues.

Some work has been done this year on re-numbering, particularly of individual coins - but not of the section of sets.

The prices in the catalogue represent the range of retail prices at which coins are being offered for sale at the time of going to press and NOT the price which a dealer will pay. These prices are based on our knowledge of the market and the current demand for particular coins. Where prices have not been given it is usually because they are very recent issues and a price has not yet been established for the secondary market. In addition to this, many coins are only issued as part of sets so prices for the individual coins are not relevant as they rarely appear in commerce.

In many cases the precious metal content of the coin is a major factor in deciding its value so the price of many coins will fluctuate with the value of the metal content.

Thank you to those of you who have contacted us with corrections and suggestions; we continue to welcome feedback from readers. Our aim is to make this catalogue evermore accurate and user-friendly so please feel free to write to us at Spink with your comments.

Happy collecting

Geoff Kitchen
Editor, Decimal Issues

INTRODUCTION

The decision to adopt decimal currency was announced in March 1966 following the recommendation of the Halsbury Committee of Enquiry which had been appointed in 1961. The date for the introduction of the new system was 15 February 1971 and it was evident that the Royal Mint facilities which had been located on Tower Hill for more than 150 years would be unable to strike the significant quantities of coins required on that site. The Government therefore decided to build a new mint at Llantrisant in South Wales.

The new system provided for three smaller bronze coins with the denominations of a half new penny, one new penny and two new pence, and very large numbers were struck and stockpiled for D-Day. The cupro-nickel five and ten new pence denominations with the same specifications as the shilling and florin were introduced in 1968 and circulated along side the former denominations. A further change was the introduction in 1969 of a 50 new pence coin to replace the ten shilling banknote.

In 1982 and 1983 two more new coins were introduced; the 20 pence which helped to reduce demand for five and ten pence pieces, and the first circulating non-precious metal £1 coin which replaced the bank note of the same value. 1982 also saw the removal of the word "NEW" from all denominations from half penny to 50 pence.

Increasing raw material costs and inflation also play a part in the development of a modern coinage system, and smaller five and ten pence coins were introduced in 1990 and 1992 respectively. A further change in 1992 was the use of copper plated steel for the one and two pence bronze coins. The plated steel coins are magnetic unlike the solid bronze alloy. Changes were also made in 1997 when the 50 pence coin was reduced in size and a bimetallic circulating £2 was also introduced to reduce demand for the £1 value.

As we have a token coinage where the intrinsic metal content is less than the nominal face value, the cost of production has to be reviewed. The cupro-nickel alloy five pence and ten pence coins were therefore replaced in 2012 in nickel plated steel. A further change will take place in 2017 when the £1 coin will be replaced by a bi-metallic version with a new design. The specification will have security features that will combat the production of counterfeit coins, which have become a problem over several years. The new coin will however present problems for companies that need to convert vending machines which accept £1 coins.

In 2008, 40 years after the introduction of the first of the decimal coin designs, a completely new series was issued. After an open competition that attracted more than 4,000 entries, designs by a young graphic designer, Matthew Dent, were selected, and represent a somewhat radical approach that uses elements of the shield of the Royal Arms for the denominations of 50 pence to one pence. The £1 shows the complete shield. Interestingly none of the coins show the value in numerical form.

The Mint offered sets of the new designs in various metals and qualities, and also gave collectors an opportunity to acquire the last issues of the original series. These, together with various commemorative issues, present collectors with a significant and varied range, and illustrate the importance of the sales of special issues to the Mint's business.

In the 40 years since Decimalisation there have been changes to the obverse portrait of Her Majesty The Queen with the exception of the Silver Maundy coins which retain the Mary Gillick design. The new effigy for the introduction of the decimal series was by Arnold Machin, followed then by Raphael Maklouf, Ian Rank-Broadley and now with a new portrait by Jody Clark.

The change in the layout that was introduced previously allowed collectors to see coins by denomination rather than by portrait, but gave rise to problems regarding numbering. This, coupled with the many new issues from the Royal Mint, has required a major re-think. A new sequence has therefore been introduced for individual coins, but the sets sections will be dealt with later.

BRONZE

HALF PENCE COINS
Obverse portrait by Arnold Machin

A1   A2

A1   **Half new penny.** R. The Royal Crown and the inscription '1/2 NEW PENNY'
(Reverse design: Christopher Ironside)

1971..................... £0.50	1975...........................£0.50	1979.........................£0.50
— Proof *FDC*...... £1	— Proof *FDC* £1	— Proof *FDC*......... £1
1972 Proof *FDC* £2	1976...........................£0.50	1980.........................£0.50
1973..................... £0.50	— Proof *FDC* £1	— Proof *FDC*..........£1
— Proof *FDC*...... £1	1977...........................£0.50	1981.........................£0.50
1974..................... £0.50	— Proof *FDC* £1	— Proof *FDC* £1
— Proof *FDC*...... £1	1978...........................£0.50	
	— Proof *FDC* £1	

A2   **Half penny.** 'New' omitted. As illustration

1982..................... £0.50	1983...........................£0.50	1984*...........................£2
— Proof *FDC*...... £1	— Proof *FDC* £1	— Proof *FDC*..........£2

ONE PENCE COINS
Obverse portrait by Arnold Machin

B1   B2   B3

B1   **One new penny.** R. A portcullis with chains royally crossed, being the badge of Henry
VII and his successors, and the inscription 'NEW PENNY' above and the figure '1' below.
(Design: Christopher Ironside)

1971..................... £0.50	1975 .... £0.50	1979.........................£0.50
— Proof *FDC*...... £1	— Proof *FDC* £1	— Proof *FDC*..........£1
1972 Proof *FDC* £2	1976........................... £0.50	1980.........................£0.50
1973..................... £0.50	— Proof *FDC* £1	— Proof *FDC*..........£1
— Proof *FDC* £1	1977 .... £0.50	1981.........................£0.50
1974..................... £0.50	— Proof *FDC* £1	— Proof *FDC* £1
— Proof *FDC* £1	1978 .... £0.50	
	— Proof *FDC* £1	

B2   **One penny.** 'New' omitted, As illustration

1982..................... £0.50	1983 .... £0.50	1984.............................£1
— Proof *FDC*....... £1	— *FDC* £1	— Proof *FDC*..........£1

Obverse portrait by Raphael Maklouf
B3   **One penny.** R. Crowned portcullis with chains

1985..................... £0.50	1988...........................£0.50	1991.........................£0.50
— Proof *FDC* £1	— Proof *FDC* £1	— Proof *FDC*..........£1
1986..................... £0.50	1989...........................£0.50	1992.........................£0.50
— Proof *FDC*........ £1	— Proof *FDC* £1	— Proof *FDC*..........£1
1987...............................	1990	
— Proof *FDC*........ £1	— Proof *FDC* ....,£1	

* Coins marked thus were originally issued in Royal Mint sets.

COPPER PLATED STEEL

B4 **One penny** R. Crowned portcullis with chains

1992...................... £0.50	1995 ....£0.50	1997......................... £0.50
1993...................... £0.50	— Proof *FDC** £1	— Proof *FDC** £1
— Proof *FDC** £1	1996 ....£0.50	
1994...................... £0.50	— Proof *FDC** £1	
— Proof *FDC**....... £1	— Proof in silver *FDC**£15	

Obverse portrait by Ian Rank-Broadley

B5

B5 One penny. R. Crowned portcullis with chains. (Illus. as 4381)

1998..£1	2004.. £1
— Proof *FDC* * £3	— Proof *FDC*.....................................£3
1999..£1	2005.. £1
— Proof *FDC* * £3	— Proof *FDC*.....................................£3
2000..£1	2006.. £1
— Proof *FDC* * £3	— Proof *FDC*.....................................£3
— Proof in silver FDC (see PSS08)* £8	— Proof in silver *FDC* (see PSS22)* ... £8
2001..£1	2007.. £1
— Proof *FDC* * £3	— Proof *FDC* * £3
2002..£1	2008.. £1
— Proof *FDC* * £3	— Proof *FDC* * £3
— Proof in gold *FDC* (see PGJS1)*£200	— Proof in silver *FDC* (see PSS27)* ... £8
2003..£1	— Proof in gold *FDC* (see PGEBCS)*£250
— Proof *FDC* * £3	— Proof in platinum *FDC*
	(see PPEBCS)* £300

B6

B6 **One penny.** R. A section of Our Royal Arms showing elements of the first and third quartering accompanied by the words 'ONE PENNY'(Reverse design: Matthew Dent)

2008 ....£3
—   Proof *FDC* (in 2008 set, see PS96)* £3
—   Proof in silver *FDC* (in 2008 set, see PSS28)* £8
—   Proof piedfort in silver *FDC* (in 2008 set, see PSS29)* £15
—   Proof in gold *FDC* (in 2008 set, see PGRSAS)* £250
—   Proof in platinum *FDC* (in 2008 set, see PPRSAS)*............................£300

2009
—   Proof *FDC* (in 2009 set, see PS97)*
—   BU in silver £15
—   Proof in silver *FDC* (in 2009 set, see PSS 37)* £15

* *Coins marked thus were originally issued in Royal Mint sets.*

2010
— Proof *FDC* (in 2010 set, see PS101)* £3
— BU in silver £15
— Proof in silver *FDC* (in 2010 set, Edition: 3,500, see PSS41)* £15
2011 ....£3
— Proof *FDC* (in 2011 set, see PS104) * £3
— BU in silver..£15
— Proof in silver *FDC* (in 2011 set, Edition: 2,500, see PSS44)*............................£15
2012 ....£3
— Proof *FDC* (in 2012 set, see PS107) * £3
— BU in silver..£23
— Proof in silver *FDC* (Edition: 995, see PSS47)* £30
— Proof in silver with selected gold plating *FDC* (Edition: 2,012, see PSS48) * £30
— Proof in gold *FDC* (Edition: 150 see PGDJS)*...£250
2013 ....£3
— Proof *FDC* (in 2013 set, see PS109)* £5
— BU in silver £23
— Proof in silver *FDC* (Edition: 2,013, see PSS50)*...£30
— Proof in gold *FDC* (Issued: 59 see PGCAS)*...£250
2014..£5
— Proof *FDC* (in 2014 set, see PS112)*
— Proof in silver *FDC* (Edition: 2014 see PSS57)*
2015
— Proof *FDC* (in 2015 set, see PS115) * £5
— Proof in silver *FDC* (Edition: 7,500 see PSS62)*...£30
— Proof in gold *FDC* (Edition: 500 see PGC4P) * £225

Obverse portrait by Jody Clark
B7   One penny.
2015
— Proof *FDC* (in 2015 set, see PS116) * £5
— Proof in silver *FDC* (Edition: 7,500 see PSS63)*
— Proof in gold *FDC* (Edition: 500 see PGC5P) *
2016
— Proof *FDC* (in 2016 set, see PSS119)*
— Proof in silver *FDC* (Edition: 1,500 see PSS68)*

* Coins marked thus were originally issued in Royal Mint sets.

BRONZE

TWO PENCE COINS
Obverse portrait by Arnold Machin

C1   C2

C1 **Two new pence.** R. The badge of the Prince of Wales, being three ostrich feathers enfiling a coronet of cross pattee and fleur de lys, with the motto 'ICH DIEN', and the inscription '2 NEW PENCE' (Reverse design: Christopher Ironside)

1971...................... £0.50	1976............................£0.50	1979.......................... £0.50
— Proof *FDC*...... £1	— Proof *FDC* £1	— Proof *FDC*...........£1
1972 Proof *FDC*...... £2	1977............................£0.50	1980.......................... £0.50
1973 Proof *FDC*...... £2	— Proof *FDC* £1	— Proof *FDC*...........£1
1974 Proof *FDC*...... £2	1978............................£0.50	1981.......................... £0.50
1975...................... £0.50	— Proof *FDC* £1	— Proof *FDC*...........£1
— Proof *FDC*....... £1		

C2 **Two pence.** 'New' omitted. As illustration

1982*......................... £1	1983*..............................£1	1984*............................£1
— Proof *FDC*....... £2	— Proof *FDC* £2	— Proof *FDC*...........£2

C2A — **Error reverse.** The word 'new' was dropped from the reverse of the currency issues in 1982 but a number of 2 pence coins were struck in 1983 with the incorrect reverse die, similar to coins listed as 4235. Reports suggest that the error coins, or 'Mules' were contained in some sets packed by the Royal Mint for Martini issued in 1983 ....£750

Obverse portrait by Raphael Maklouf

C3

C3 **Two pence.** R. Prince of Wales feathers

1985...................... £0.50	1988............................ £0.50	1991..........................£0.50
— Proof *FDC*........ £1	— Proof *FDC* £1	— Proof *FDC*...........£1
1986...................... £0.50	1989............................ £0.50	1992..........................£0.50
— Proof *FDC*........ £1	— Proof *FDC* £1	— Proof *FDC*...........£1
1987...................... £0.50	1990............................ £0.50	
— Proof *FDC*........ £1	— Proof *FDC* £1	

* Coins marked thus were originally issued in Royal Mint sets.

COPPER PLATED STEEL

C4 **Two pence** R. Plumes

1992............£1	1995............£1	1997............£0.50
1993............£1	— Proof *FDC**............£1	— Proof *FDC**............£1
— Proof *FDC**.......£1	1996............£1	
1994............£1	— Proof *FDC**............£1	
— Proof *FDC**........£1	— Proof in silver *FDC**£15	

Obverse portrait by Ian Rank-Broadley

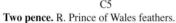

C5   C6

C5 **Two pence.** R. Prince of Wales feathers.

1998............£1	2004............£1
— Proof *FDC**............£3	— Proof *FDC**............£3
1999............£1	2005............£1
— Proof *FDC**............£3	— Proof *FDC**............£3
2000............£1	2006............£1
— Proof *FDC**............£3	— Proof *FDC**............£3
— Proof in silver FDC (see PSS08)* £8	— Proof in silver *FDC* (see PSS22)*..........£8
2001............£1	2007............£1
— Proof *FDC**............£3	— Proof *FDC**............£3
2002............£1	2008............£1
— Proof *FDC**............£3	— Proof *FDC**............£3
— Proof in gold *FDC* (see PGJS1)*£400	— Proof in silver *FDC* (see PSS27)*........£10
2003	— Proof in gold *FDC* (see PGEBCS)* ... £500
— Proof *FDC**............£3	— Proof in platinum *FDC*
	(see PPEBCS)*............£550

C6 **Two pence.** R. A section of Our Royal Arms showing elements of the second quartering accompanied by the words 'TWO PENCE'(Reverse design: Matthew Dent)

2008............£3	
— Proof *FDC* (in 2008 set, see PS96)*............£3	
— Proof in silver *FDC* (in 2008 set, see PSS28)*............£10	
— Proof piedfort in silver *FDC* (in 2008 set, see PSS29)*............£20	
— Proof in gold *FDC* (in 2008 set, see PGRSAS)*............£500	
— Proof in platinum *FDC* (in 2008 set, see PPRSAS)*............£550	
2009............£3	
— Proof *FDC* (in 2009 set, see PS97)*............£3	
— Proof in silver *FDC* (in 2009 set, see PSS 37)*............£10	
2010............£3	
— Proof *FDC* (in 2010 set, see PS101)*............£3	
— Proof in silver *FDC* (in 2010 set, Edition: 3,500 see PSS41)*............£10	
2011............£3	
— Proof *FDC* (in 2011 set, see PS104) *............£3	
— Proof in silver *FDC* (in 2011 set, Edition: 2,500, see PSS44) *............£15	

* Coins marked thus were originally issued in Royal Mint sets.

2012.. £3
— Proof *FDC* (in 2012 set, see PS107)* £3
— Proof in silver *FDC* (Edition: 995, see PSS47)*.............................. £30
— Proof in silver with selected gold plating *FDC* (Edition: 2,012, see PSS48) * £30
— Proof in gold *FDC* (Edition: 150 see PGDJS)* £500
2013.. £3
— Proof *FDC* (in 2013 set, see PS110)* £5
— Proof in silver *FDC* (Edition: 2,013, see PSS50)*........................... £30
— Proof in gold *FDC* (Issued: 59 see PGCAS)*.................................£500
2014.. £3
— Proof *FDC* (in 2014 set, see PS112)* £5
— Proof in silver *FDC* (Edition : 2,014 see PSS57)*
2015
— Proof *FDC* (in 2015 set, see PS115)* £5
— Proof in silver *FDC* (Edition: 7,500 see PSS62)*............................ £30
— Proof in gold *FDC* (Edition: 500 see PGC4P) * £500

Obverse portrait by Jody Clark
C7   Two pence.
2015
— Proof *FDC* (in 2015 set, see PS116)* £5
— Proof in silver *FDC* (Edition: 7,500 see PSS63)*
— Proof in gold *FDC* (Edition: 500 see PGC5P)*
2016
— Proof *FDC* (in 2016 set, see PSS119)*
— Proof in silver *FDC* (Edition: 1,500 see PSS68)*

CUPRO-NICKEL

FIVE PENCE COINS
Obverse portrait by Arnold Machin

D1   D2

D1   Five new pence. R. A thistle royally crowned, being the badge of Scotland, and the inscription '5 NEW PENCE' (Reverse design: Christopher Ironside)

1968...................... £0.50	1974 Proof *FDC** £4	1979.......................... £0.50
1969...................... £0.50	1975 ....£0.50	— Proof *FDC**...........£2
1970...................... £0.50	— Proof *FDC** £2	1980.......................... £0.50
1971...................... £0.50	1976 Proof *FDC** £4	— Proof *FDC**...........£2
— Proof *FDC**....... £2	1977 .... £0.50	1981 Proof *FDC**..........£4
1972 Proof *FDC**...... £4	— Proof *FDC** £2	
1973 Proof *FDC**...... £4	1978 .... £0.50	
	— Proof *FDC** £2	

D2   Five pence. 'New' omitted. As illustration

1982*......................... £2	1983*.............................£2	1984*...........................£2
— Proof *FDC**....... £4	— Proof *FDC** £4	— Proof *FDC**...........£4

* Coins marked thus were originally issued in Royal Mint sets.

Obverse portrait by Raphael Maklouf

D3   D4

D3   **Five pence.** R. Crowned thistle
1985* .... £2   1988 ....£1   1990* £2
—   Proof *FDC* .... £4   —   Proof *FDC* ....£2   —   Proof *FDC* £2
1986* .... £2   1989 ....£1   —   Proof in silver *FDC* £12
—   Proof *FDC* .... £4   —   Proof *FDC* £2
1987 .... £1
—   Proof *FDC* £2

D4   **Five pence.** R. Crowned thistle: reduced diameter of 18mm
1990 ....£1   1992 ....£1   —   Proof *FDC* £2
—   Proof *FDC* ....£2   —   Proof *FDC* ....£2   1996 ....£1
—   Proof in silver *FDC* £10   1993* ....£2   —   Proof *FDC* £2
—   Proof piedfort in silver   —   Proof *FDC* ....£4   —   Proof in silver *FDC* £15
    FDC (Issued:20,000)£20   1994 ....£1   1997 ....£1
1991 ....£1   —   Proof *FDC* ....£2   —   Proof *FDC* £2
—   Proof *FDC* ....£2   1995 ....£1

Obverse portrait by Ian Rank-Broadley

D5

D5   **Five pence.** R. Crowned thistle
1998 .... £1   2004 ....£1
—   Proof *FDC* * .... £3   —   Proof *FDC* £3
1999 .... £1   2005 ....£1
—   Proof *FDC* * .... £3   —   Proof *FDC* £3
2000 .... £1   2006 ....£1
—   Proof *FDC* * .... £3   —   Proof *FDC* £3
—   Proof in silver FDC (see PSS08)*£12   —   Proof in silver *FDC* (see PSS22)* £12
2001 .... £1   2007 ....£1
—   Proof *FDC* * .... £3   —   Proof *FDC* £3
2002 .... £1   2008 ....£1
—   Proof *FDC* * .... £3   —   Proof *FDC* * £3
—   Proof in gold *FDC* (see PGJS1) £225   —   Proof in silver *FDC* (see PSS27)* £12
2003 .... £1   —   Proof in gold *FDC* (see PGEBCS)* £225
—   Proof *FDC* * .... £3   —   Proof in platinum *FDC*
                                                                  (see PPEBCS)* £325

* Coins marked thus were originally issued in Royal Mint sets

D6

D6   **Five pence.** R. A section of Our Royal Arms showing elements of all four quarterings accompanied by the words 'FIVE PENCE'(Reverse design: Matthew Dent)

2008...£3
— Proof *FDC* (in 2008 set, see PS96)*...£3
— Proof in silver *FDC* (in 2008 set, see PSS28)*...£12
— Proof piedfort in silver *FDC* (in 2008 set, see PSS29)*............................£25
— Proof in gold *FDC* (in 2008 set, see PGRSAS)*.......................................£225
— Proof in platinum *FDC* (in 2008 set, see PPRSAS)*.................................£325
2009...£1
— Proof *FDC* (in 2009 set, see PS97)*...£3
— Proof in silver *FDC* (in 2009 set, see PSS 37 ....£12
2010...£1
— Proof *FDC* (in 2010 set, see PS101)*...£3
— Proof in silver *FDC* (in 2010 set, Edition: 3,500 see PSS41)*...............£12
2011...£3
— Proof *FDC* (in 2011 set, see PS104)*...£3
— Proof in silver *FDC* (in 2011 set, Edition: 2,500, see PSS44)* £12

NICKEL PLATED STEEL
D7   **Five pence.**
2012...£3
— Proof *FDC* (in 2012 set, see PS107)* £5
— Proof in silver *FDC* (Edition: 995, see PSS47)*.......................................£30
— Proof in silver with selected gold plating *FDC* (Edition: 2,012, see PSS48)*.......£30
— Proof in gold *FDC* (Edition: 150 see PGDJS)* £225
2013... £3
— Proof *FDC* (in 2013 set, see PS109)* £5
— Proof in silver *FDC* (Edition: 2,013, see PSS50)* £30
— Proof in gold *FDC* (Issued: 59 see PGCAS)* £225
2014
— Proof *FDC* (in 2014 set, see PS112)*.. £5
— Proof in silver *FDC* (Edition: 2,014 see PSS57)*
2015
— Proof *FDC* (in 2015 set, see PS115)* £5
— Proof in silver *FDC* (Edition: 7,500 see PSS62)*.....................................£30
— Proof in gold *FDC* (Edition: 500 see PGC4P)* £225

* *Coins marked thus were originally issued in Royal Mint sets.*

Obverse portrait by Jody Clark

D8

D8   Five pence.
2015
— Proof *FDC* (in 2015 set, see PS116)* £5
— Proof in silver *FDC* (Edition: 7,500 see PSS63)*
— Proof in gold *FDC* (Edition: 500 see PGC5P)*
2016
— Proof *FDC* (in 2016 set, see PSS119)*
— Proof in silver *FDC* (Edition: 1,500 see PSS68)*

SIX PENCE COIN

E1

E1   Six pence. R. A design of Our Royal Cypher surrounded by a floral motif with the inscription SIXPENCE' accompanied by the date of the year. (Reverse design: John Bergdahl)
2016
— -Specimen in presentation box £30

TEN PENCE COINS
Obverse portrait by Arnold Machin

F1

F1   Ten new pence. R. Lion passant guardant being royally crowned, being part of the crest of England, and the inscription 'Ten New Pence' (Reverse design: Christopher Ironside)

1968..................... £0.50	1974.......................... £0.50	1978 Proof *FDC*...........£4
1969..................... £0.50	— Proof *FDC** £3	1979..........................£0.50
1970..................... £0.50	1975 .... £0.50	— Proof *FDC*............ £3
1971..................... £0.50	— Proof *FDC** £3	1980..............................£1
— Proof *FDC**....... £3	1976 .... £0.50	— Proof *FDC**...........£3
1972 Proof *FDC**...... £4	— Proof *FDC** £3	1981..............................£1
1973...................... 0.40	1977 .... 0.50	— Proof *FDC**...........£3
— Proof *FDC**....... £3	— Proof *FDC** £3	

* Coins marked thus were originally issued in Royal Mint sets.

F2

F2   **Ten pence.** 'New' omitted. As illustration

1982*.........................£3	1983*.............................£3	1984*.............................£3
— Proof *FDC*.......£4	— Proof *FDC*............£4	— Proof *FDC*............£4

Obverse portrait by Raphael Maklouf

F3

F3   **Ten pence.** R. Lion passant guardant

1985*.............................£3	1988*.............................£3	1991*.............................£4
— Proof *FDC* £4	— Proof *FDC*.............£4	— Proof *FDC*...........£4
1986*.............................£3	1989*.............................£4	1992*.............................£3
— Proof *FDC*........£4	— Proof *FDC*.............£4	— Proof *FDC*...........£4
1987*.............................£3	1990*.............................£4	— Proof in silver *FDC** £14
— Proof *FDC*........£4	— Proof *FDC*.............£4	

F4

F4   **Ten pence** R Lion passant guardant: reduced diameter of 24.5mm

1992...£1	1995.......................................£1
— Proof *FDC*....................................£3	— Proof *FDC*...................£3
— Proof in silver *FDC** £10....................	1996.......................................£1
— Proof piedfort in silver *FDC** (Issued: 14,167)£30	— Proof *FDC*....................£3
1993*...£3	— Proof in silver *FDC**...£15
— Proof *FDC*....................................£4	1997.......................................£1
1994*...£3	— Proof *FDC*....................£3
— Proof *FDC*....................................£4	

* *Coins marked thus were originally issued in Royal Mint sets.*

F5   F6

Obverse portrait by Ian Rank-Broadley

F5   **Ten pence.** R. Lion passant guardant. (Illus. as 4232)

1998*...............................£3	2004 ....£1
— Proof *FDC*...........................£4	— Proof *FDC* £3
1999*...............................£3	2005 ....£1
— Proof *FDC*...........................£4	— Proof *FDC* £3
2000...............................£1	2006 ....£1
— Proof *FDC*...........................£3	— Proof *FDC* £3
— Proof in silver FDC (see PSS08)* £15	— Proof in silver *FDC* (see PSS22)*..........£15
2001...............................£1	2007 ....£1
— Proof *FDC*...........................£3	— Proof *FDC* £3
2002...............................£1	2008 ....£1
— Proof *FDC*...........................£3	— Proof *FDC* £3
— Proof in gold *FDC* (see PGJS1)*£500	— Proof in silver *FDC* (see PSS27)* £15
2003...............................£1	— Proof in gold *FDC* (see PGEBCS)* £500
— Proof *FDC*...........................£3	— Proof in platinum *FDC*
	(see PPEBCS)*...........................£650

F6   **Ten pence.** R. A section of Our Royal Arms showing elements of the first quartering accompanied by the words 'TEN PENCE'(Reverse design: Matthew Dent)

2008...£3
— Proof *FDC* (in 2008 set, see PS96)*...£6
— Proof in silver *FDC* (in 2008 set, see PSS28)*...£15
— Proof piedfort in silver *FDC* (in 2008 set, see PSS29)*...£25
— Proof in gold *FDC* (in 2008 set, see PGRSAS)*...£500
— Proof in platinum *FDC* (in 2008 set, see PPRSAS)*..£650
2009...£3
— Proof *FDC* (in 2009 set, see PS97)*...£6
— Proof in silver *FDC* (in 2009 set, see PSS 37)*...£15
2010...£3
— Proof *FDC* (in 2010 set, see PS101)*...£6
— Proof in silver *FDC* (in 2010 set, Edition: 3,500 see PSS 41)*.............................£15
2011...£3
— Proof *FDC* (in 2011 set, see PS104) *...£3
— Proof in silver *FDC* (in 2011 set, Edition: 2,500, see PSS44) *....................................£15

* *Coins marked thus were originally issued in Royal Mint sets.*

NICKEL PLATED STEEL

F7   **Ten pence.**

2012..£3
— Proof *FDC* (in 2012 set, see PS107)* £3
— Proof in silver *FDC* (Edition: 995, see PSS47)*...................................£30
— Proof in silver with selected gold plating *FDC* (Edition: 2,012, see PSS48)*.......£30
— Proof in gold *FDC* (Edition: 150 see PGDJS)* £500

2013..£3
— Proof *FDC* (in 2013 set, see PS109)* £5
— Proof in silver *FDC* (Edition: 2,013, see PSS50)* £30
— Proof in gold *FDC* (Issued: 59 see PGCAS)*....................................£450

2014
— Proof *FDC* (in 2014 set, see PS112)* £5
— Proof in silver *FDC* (Edition: 2,014 see PSS57)*

2015
— Proof *FDC* (in 2015 set, see PS115)* £5
— Proof in silver *FDC* (Edition: 7,500 see PSS62)* £30
— Proof in gold *FDC* (Edition: 500 see PGC4P)*....................................£500

Obverse portrait by Jody Clark

F8

F8   **Ten pence.**

2015
— Proof *FDC* (in 2015 set, see PS116)* £5
— Proof in silver *FDC* (Edition: 7,500 see PSS63)..£30
— Proof in gold *FDC* (Edition: 500 see PGC5P)* £500

2016
— Proof *FDC* (in 2016 set, see PSS119)*
— Proof in silver *FDC* (Edition: 1,500 see PSS68)*

* Coins marked thus were originally issued in Royal Mint sets.

CUPRO-NICKEL

TWENTY PENCE COINS
Obverse portrait by Arnold Machin

G1

G1 **Twenty pence.** R. The Royal Badge of the Rose of England represented as a double rose
barbed and seeded, slipped and leaved and ensigned by a Royal Crown and the date of the
year with the inscription 'TWENTY PENCE' and the figure '20' superimposed on the stem
of the rose.(Reverse design: William Gardner)

1982...£0.50
—   Proof *FDC**..£3
—   Proof piedfort in silver *FDC* (Issued: 10,000) £30
1983...£0.50
1984...£0.50
—   Proof *FDC**..£3

Obverse portrait by Raphael Maklouf

G2

G2 **Twenty pence.** R. Crowned double rose

1985............................ £1	1990 ....£1	1995...............................£1
— Proof *FDC**........ £3	— Proof *FDC** £3	— Proof *FDC**...........£3
1986*........................ £3	1991 ....£1	1996...............................£1
— Proof *FDC**........ £4	— Proof *FDC** £3	— Proof *FDC**...........£3
1987 ....£1	1992...............................£1	— Proof in silver *FDC** £18
— Proof *FDC** £3	— Proof *FDC** £3	1997...............................£1
1988........................... £1	1993 ....£1	— Proof *FDC**...........£3
— Proof *FDC**........ £3	— Proof *FDC** £3	
1989........................... £1	1994 ....£1	
— Proof *FDC**........ £3	— Proof *FDC** £3	

* *Coins marked thus were originally issued in Royal Mint sets.*

Obverse portrait by Ian Rank-Broadley

G3

G3   **Twenty pence.** R. Crowned double rose.

1998... £1	2004 .... £1
— Proof *FDC*............................... £3	— Proof *FDC* £3
1999... £1	2005 .... £1
— Proof *FDC*............................... £3	— Proof *FDC* £3
2000... £1	2006 .... £1
— Proof *FDC*............................... £3	— Proof *FDC* £3
— Proof in silver *FDC* (see PSS08) *£20	— Proof in silver *FDC* (see PSS22)* £20
2001... £1	2007 .... £1
— Proof *FDC*............................... £3	— Proof *FDC* £3
2002... £1	2008 .... £1
— Proof *FDC*............................... £3	— Proof *FDC* £3
— Proof in gold *FDC* (see PGJS1)*£450	— Proof in silver *FDC* (see PSS27)*..........£20
2003... £1	— Proof in gold *FDC* (see PGEBCS)* £350
— Proof *FDC*............................... £3	— Proof in platinum *FDC* (see PPEBCS)* £550

G4

G4   **Twenty pence.** R. A section of Our Royal Arms showing elements of the second and forth quartering accompanied by the words 'TWENTY PENCE'(Reverse design: Matthew Dent)

2008...£3
— Proof *FDC* (in 2008 set, see PS96)*...£3
— Proof in silver *FDC* (in 2008 set, see PSS28)*..£20
— Proof piedfort in silver *FDC* (in 2008 set, see PSS29)* £40
— Proof in gold *FDC* (in 2008 set, see PGRSAS)* £350
— Proof in platinum *FDC* (in 2008 set, see PPRSAS)*....................................£550
2009...£3
— Proof *FDC* (in 2009 set, see PS97)*...£6
— Proof in silver *FDC* (in 2009 set, see PSS 37)*..£20
2010...£3
— Proof *FDC* (in 2010 set, see PS101)*...£6
— Proof in silver *FDC* (in 2010 set, Edition: 3,500 see PSS 41)*...................£20
2011...£3
— Proof *FDC* (in 2011 set, see PS104) *...£3
— Proof in silver *FDC* (in 2011 set, Edition: 2,500, see PSS44)*....................£15

* Coins marked thus were originally issued in Royal Mint sets.

2012...£3
— Proof *FDC* (in 2012 set, see PS107)* £3
— Proof in silver *FDC* (Edition: 995, see PSS47)*....................................£30
— Proof in silver with selected gold plating *FDC* (Edition: 2,012, see PSS48)*.......£30
— Proof in gold *FDC* (Edition: 150 see PGDJS)* £350
2013...£3
— Proof *FDC* (in 2013 set, see PS109)*..£5
— Proof in silver *FDC* (Edition: 2,013, see PSS50)* £30
— Proof in gold *FDC* (Issued: 59 see PGCAS)*......................................£350
2014
— Proof *FDC* (in 2014 set, see PS112)*...£5
— Proof in silver *FDC* (Edition: 2,014 see PSS57)*

2015
— Proof *FDC* (in 2015 set, see PS115)*...£5
— Proof in silver *FDC* (Edition: 7,500 see PSS62)* £30
— Proof in gold *FDC* (Edition: 500 see PGC4P)*.....................................£350

G4A — **Error obverse – known as a Mule.** The new reverse design by Matthew Dent does not include the year date and this should have appeared on the obverse. A number of coins were struck using the undated obverse die that had previously been used with the dated reverse of the crowned double rose. (See Illus. G3)..£100

Obverse portrait by Jody Clark

G5

G5   **Twenty pence.**
2015
— Proof *FDC* (in 2015 set, see PS116)* £5
— Proof in silver *FDC* (Edition: 7,500 see PSS63)*
— Proof in gold *FDC* (Edition: 500 see PGC5P)*
2016
— Proof *FDC* (in 2016 set, see PSS119)*
— Proof in silver *FDC* (Edition: 1,500 see PSS68)*

* Coins marked thus were originally issued in Royal Mint sets.

FIFTY PENCE COINS
Obverse portrait by Arnold Machin

H1

H1   **Fifty new pence** (seven-sided). R. A figure of Britannia seated beside a lion, with a shield resting against her right side, holding a trident in her right hand and an olive branch in her left hand; and the inscription '50 NEW PENCE'. (Reverse design: Christopher Ironside)

1969............................£3	1976................................£2	1979..............................£2
1970............................£4	— Proof *FDC** £3	— Proof *FDC**...........£3
1971 Proof *FDC**.......£5	1977................................£2	1980..............................£2
1972 Proof *FDC**.......£5	— Proof *FDC** £3	— Proof *FDC**...........£3
1974 Proof *FDC**.......£5	1978................................£2	1981..............................£2
1975 Proof *FDC**.......£5	— Proof *FDC** £3	— Proof *FDC**...........£3

H2   H3

H2   Accession to European Economic Community. R. The inscription 'FIFTY PENCE' and the date of the year, surrounded by nine hands, symbolizing the nine members of the community, clasping one another in a mutual gesture of trust, assistance and friendship. (Reverse design: David Wynne)

1973..£3
—   Proof *FDC* **...£6

H2A   —Design as H2 above, but struck in very small numbers in silver on thicker blank. Sometimes referred to as a piedfort but not twice the weight of the regular cupro-nickel currency issue. The pieces were presented to EEC Finance Ministers and possibly senior officials on the occasion of the United Kingdom joining the European Economic Community..£2500

H3   **Fifty pence.** 'New' omitted. As illustration

1982............................£3	1983................................£2	1984*..............................£3
— Proof *FDC**........£3	— Proof *FDC** £3	— Proof *FDC**...........£3

* Coins marked thus were originally issued in Royal Mint sets
** Issued as an individual proof coin and in the year set

Obverse portrait by Raphael Maklouf

H4

H4 **Fifty pence.** R. Britannia

1985..........£3	1990*.............£4	1996*.............£3
— Proof *FDC*......£3	— Proof *FDC*..........£5	— Proof *FDC*..........£4
1986*.............£3	1991*.............£4	— Proof in silver *FDC** £20
— Proof *FDC*......£3	— Proof *FDC*..........£5	1997.............£2
1987*.............£3	1992*.............£4	— Proof *FDC*..........£4
— Proof *FDC*..........£3	— Proof *FDC*..........£5	— Proof in silver *FDC**£20
1988*.............£3	1993*.............£4	
— Proof *FDC*......£4	— Proof *FDC*..........£4	
1989*.............£4	1995*.............£3	
— Proof *FDC*......£3	— Proof *FDC*..........£4	

H5

H5 **Fifty pence** Presidency of the Council of European Community Ministers and completion of the Single Market. R A representation of a table on which are placed twelve stars, linked by a network of lines to each other and also to twelve chairs, around the table, on one of which appear the letters 'UK', and with the dates '1992' and '1993' above and the value '50 PENCE' below. (Reverse design: Mary Milner Dickens)

1992-1993 ....£12
— Proof *FDC*..£12
— Proof in silver *FDC** (Issued: 26,890 .... £28
— Proof piedfort in silver *FDC* (Issued: 10,993) £60
— Proof in gold *FDC* (Issued: 1,864)..£1000

* Coins marked thus were originally issued in Royal Mint sets

H6

H6   **Fifty pence** 50th Anniversary of the Normandy Landings on D-Day. R: A design representing the Allied invasion force of the D-Day landings heading for Normandy and filling the sea and sky, Together with the value '50 PENCE' (Reverse design: John Mills)
1994...£3
—   Specimen in presentation folder...£5
—   Proof *FDC**..£5
—   Proof in silver *FDC* (Issued: 40,000)..£35
—   Proof piedfort in silver *FDC* (Issued: 10,000) £60
—   Proof in gold *FDC* (Issued: 1,877)..£1100

H7   **Fifty penc**e R. Britannia: reduced diameter of 27.3mm
1997...£2
—   Proof *FDC**..£4
—   Proof in silver *FDC* (Issued: 1,632)..£25
—   Proof piedfort in silver *FDC* (Issued: 7,192) £40

Obverse portrait by Ian Rank-Broadley

H8

H8   **Fifty pence.** R. Britannia. (Illus. as 4351)

1998................................... £3	2006 .... £3
— Proof *FDC**.............................. £3	— Proof *FDC** £3
1999................................... £3	— Proof in silver *FDC* (see PSS22)*..... £25
— Proof *FDC**.............................. £3	2007 .... £3
2000................................... £3	— Proof *FDC** £3
— Proof *FDC**.............................. £3	2008 .... £3
— Proof in silver *FDC* (see PSS08)*£25	— Proof *FDC** £3
2001................................... £3	— Proof in silver *FDC* (see PSS27)*....£30
— Proof *FDC**.............................. £3	— Proof in gold *FDC* (see PGEBCS)* £600
2002................................... £3	— Proof in platinum *FDC* (see PPEBCS)* £550
— Proof *FDC**.............................. £3	2009
— Proof in gold *FDC* (see PGJS1)* £450	— Proof *FDC* (in 2009 set, see PS100)* £15
2003 ....£3	— Proof in silver *FDC* (in 2009 set,
— Proof *FDC**.............................. £3	see PSS40)*.......................................£30
2004 ....£3	— Proof in gold *FDC* (in 2009 set,
— Proof *FDC** £3	see PG50PCS)*.............................. £600
2005 £3	— Proof piedfort in gold *FDC*
— Proof *FDC** £3	(see PG50PPCS)* £1200

* *Coins marked thus were originally issued in Royal Mint sets.*

H9 H10

H9 **Fifty pence.** R. Celebratory pattern of twelve stars reflecting the European flag with the dates 1973 and 1998 commemorating the 25th Anniversary of the United Kingdom's membership of the European Union and Presidency of the Council of Ministers. (Reverse design: John Mills)

1998..£2
— Proof *FDC**..£5
— Proof in silver *FDC* (Issued: 8,859)...£30
— Proof piedfort in silver *FDC* (Issued: 8,440) £60
— Proof in gold *FDC* (Issued: 1,177)..£450

2009
— Proof *FDC* (in 2009 set, see PS100)*..£15
— Proof in silver *FDC* (in 2009 set, see PSS40)*...£30
— Proof in gold *FDC* (in 2009 set, see PG50PCS)*...£600
— Proof piedfort in gold *FDC* (see PG50PPCS) *...£1200

H10 **Fifty pence.** R. A pair of hands set against a pattern of radiating lines with the words 'FIFTIETH ANNIVERSARY' and the value '50 PENCE' accompanied by the initials 'NHS' which appear five times on the outer border. (Reverse design: David Cornell)

1998..£2
— Specimen in presentation folder..£3
— Proof in silver *FDC* (Issued: 9,032)...£30
— Proof piedfort in silver *FDC* (Issued: 5,117) £60
— Proof in gold *FDC* (Issued: 651)..£600

2009
— Proof *FDC* (in 2009 set, see PS100)*..£15
— Proof in silver *FDC* (in 2009 set, see PSS40)*...£30
— Proof in gold *FDC* (in 2009 set, see PG50PCS)*...£600
— Proof piedfort in gold *FDC* (see PG50PPCS) *...£1200

* Coins marked thus were originally issued in Royal Mint sets.

H11   H12

H11   **Fifty pence.** Library commemorative. ℞. The turning pages of a book above the dates
'1850 – 2000'and the value '50 PENCE', all above a classical library building on which
the words 'PUBLIC LIBRARY' and, within the pediment , representations of compact
discs. (Reverse design: Mary Milner Dickens)

2000...£2
— Specimen in presentation folder...£5
— Proof *FDC**..£5
— Proof in silver *FDC* (Issued: 7,634)...£28
— Proof piedfort in silver *FDC* (Issued: 5,721) £60
— Proof in gold *FDC* (Issued: 710)...£600

2009
— Proof *FDC* (in 2009 set, see PS100)*...£15
— Proof in silver *FDC* (in 2009 set, see PSS40)*..£30
— Proof in gold *FDC* (in 2009 set, see PG50PCS)*..£600
— Proof piedfort in gold *FDC* (see PG50PPCS) *..£1200

H12   **Fifty pence.** Anniversary of the Suffragette Movement commemorative. ℞. The figure of
a suffragette chained to railings and holding a banner on which appear the letters 'WSPU',
to the right a ballot paper marked with a cross and the words 'GIVE WOMEN THE
VOTE', to the left the value '50 PENCE' and below and to the far right the dates '1903'
and '2003'. (Reverse design: Mary Milner Dickens)

2003..£2
— Specimen in presentation folder (Issued: 9,582).......................................£5
— Proof *FDC* (in 2003 set, see PS78)*...£5
— Proof in silver *FDC* (Issued: 6,267) £28
— Proof piedfort in silver *FDC* (Issued 6,795) £60
— Proof in gold *FDC* (Issued: 942)...£600

2009
— Proof *FDC* (in 2009 set, see PS100)*...£15
— Proof in silver *FDC* (in 2009 set, see PSS40)*..£30
— Proof in gold *FDC* (in 2009 set, see PG50PCS)*..£600
— Proof piedfort in gold *FDC* (see PG50PPCS) *..£1200

* *Coins marked thus were originally issued in Royal Mint sets.*

H13 H14 H15

H13 **Fifty pence.** 50th anniversary of the first sub four-minute mile. ℞. The legs of a running athlete with a stylised stopwatch in the background and, below, the value '50 PENCE'. (Reverse design: James Butler)

2004...£2
— Specimen in presentation folder (Issued: 10,371)...£5
— Proof *FDC* (in 2004 set, see PS81)*..£5
— Proof in silver *FDC* (Issued: 4,924)..£28
— Proof piedfort in silver *FDC* (Issued: 4,054) £60
— Proof in gold *FDC* (Issued: 644)..£600
2009
— Proof *FDC* (in 2009 set, see PS100)*...£15
— Proof in silver *FDC* (in 2009 set, seePSS40)*...£30
— Proof in gold *FDC* (in 2009 set, see PG50PCS)*..£600
— Proof piedfort in gold *FDC* (see PG50PPCS)*... £1200

H14 **Fifty pence.** 250th anniversary of the publication of Samuel Johnson's Dictionary of the English Language. ℞. Entries from Samuel Johnson's Dictionary of the English Language for the words 'FIFTY' and 'PENCE', with the figure '50' above, and the inscription 'JOHNSON'S DICTIONARY 1755' below. (Reverse design: Tom Phillips)

2005...£2
— Proof *FDC* (in 2005 set, see PS84)*..£5
— Proof in silver *FDC* (Issued: 4,029)..£28
— Proof piedfort in silver *FDC* (Issued: 3,808) £60
— Proof in gold *FDC* (Issued: 584)..£600
2009
— Proof *FDC* (in 2009 set, see PS100)*...£15
— Proof in silver *FDC* (in 2009 set, see PSS40)*...£30
— Proof in gold *FDC* (in 2009 set, see PG50PCS)*..£600
— Proof piedfort in gold *FDC* (see PG50PPCS)*... £1200

H15 **Fifty pence.** 150th anniversary of the institution of the Victoria Cross. ℞. A depiction of the obverse and reverse of a Victoria Cross with the date '29. JAN 1856' in the centre of the reverse of the Cross, the letters 'VC' to the right and the value 'FIFTY PENCE'. (Reverse design: Claire Aldridge)

2006...£2
— Specimen in presentation folder with H16...£7
— Proof *FDC* (in 2006 set, see PS87)*..£5
— Proof in silver *FDC* (Issued: 6,310)..£30
— Proof piedfort in silver *FDC* (Issued: 3,532) (see PSS27).....................................£60
— Proof in gold *FDC* (Issued: 866)..£600
2009
— Proof *FDC* (in 2009 set, see PS100)*...£15
— Proof in silver *FDC* (in 2009 set, see PSS40)*...£30
— Proof in gold *FDC* (in 2009 set, see PG50PCS)*..£600
— Proof piedfort in gold *FDC* (see PG50PPCS)*... £1200

* Coins marked thus were originally issued in Royal Mint sets.

H16   H17   H18

H16 **Fifty pence.** 150th anniversary of the institution of the Victoria Cross. R. A Depiction of
a soldier carrying a wounded comrade with an outline of the Victoria Cross surrounded
by a sunburst effect in the background and the value 'FIFTY PENCE'. (Reverse design:
Clive Duncan)

2006..£2
—   Specimen in presentation folder with H15...£7
—   Proof *FDC* (in 2006 set, see PS87)*...£5
—   Proof in silver *FDC* (Issued: 6,872)..£30
—   Proof piedfort in silver *FDC* (Issued: 3,415) (see PSS27)...................................£60
—   Proof in gold *FDC* (Issued: 804)..£600

2009
—   Proof *FDC* (in 2009 set, see PS100)*...£15
—   Proof in silver *FDC* (in 2009 set, see PSS40)*...£30
—   Proof in gold *FDC* (in 2009 set, see PG50PCS)*...£600
—   Proof piedfort in gold *FDC* (see PG50PPCS)*...£1200

H17 **Fifty pence.** Centenary of the Founding of the Scouting Movement. R. A Fleur-de-lis
superimposed over a globe and surrounded by the inscription 'BE PREPARED', and the
dates '1907' and '2007' and the denomination 'FIFTY PENCE' (Reverse design:
Kerry Jones)

2007..£2
—   Specimen in presentation folder...£7
—   Proof *FDC** (in 2007 set, see PS90)..£5
—   Proof in silver *FDC* (Issued: 10,895)..£30
—   Proof piedfort in silver *FDC** (Issued; 1,555) £60
—   Proof in gold *FDC* (Issued: 1,250) £600

2009
—   Proof *FDC* (in 2009 set, see PS100)*...£15
—   Proof in silver *FDC* (in 2009 set, see PSS40)*...£30
—   Proof in gold *FDC* (in 2009 set, see PG50PCS)*...£600
—   Proof piedfort in gold *FDC* (see PG50PPCS)*...£1200

H18 **Fifty pence.** R. A section of Our Royal Arms showing elements of the third and fourth
quarterings accompanied by the words 'FIFTY PENCE' (Reverse design: Matthew Dent)

2008..£3
—   Proof *FDC* (in 2008 set, see PS96)*...£5
—   Proof in silver *FDC* (in 2008 set, see PSS28)*...£30
—   Proof piedfort in silver *FDC* (in 2008 set, see PSS29)* £60
—   Proof in gold *FDC* (in 2008 set, see PGRSAS)* £600
—   Proof in platinum *FDC* (in 2008 set, see PPRSAS)*...£650

2009..£3
—   Proof *FDC* (in 2009 set, see PS97)*...£5
—   Proof in silver *FDC* (in 2009 set, see PSS37)*...£30
—   Proof in gold *FDC* (in 2009 set, see PG50PCS)* £600
—   Proof piedfort in gold *FDC* (see PG50PPCS)*...£1200

* Coins marked thus were originally issued in Royal Mint sets.

2010..£3
— Proof *FDC* (in 2010 set, see PS101)* £5
— Proof in silver *FDC* (in 2010 set, Edition: 3,500, see PSS41)* £30
2011 ....£3
— Proof *FDC* (in 2010 set, see PS104)*...£3
— Proof in silver *FDC* (in 2011 set, Edition: 2,500, see PSS44) *.........................£15
2012..£3
— Proof *FDC* (in 2012 set, see PS107)* £3
— Proof in silver *FDC* (Edition: 995, see PSS47)*..£30
— Proof in silver with selected gold plating *FDC* (Edition: 2,012, see PSS48) £30
— Proof in gold *FDC* (Edition: 150 see PGDJS)* £600
2013.. £3
— Proof *FDC* (in 2013 set, see PS109) * £5
— Proof in silver *FDC* (Edition: 2,013, see PSS50)*.. £30
— Proof in gold *FDC* (Issued: 59 see PGCAS)*..£600
2014
— Proof *FDC* (in 2014 set, see PS112)* £5
— Proof in silver *FDC* (Edition: 2,014 see PSS57)*
2015
— Proof *FDC* (in 2015 set, see PS115) * £5
— Proof in silver *FDC* (Edition: 7,500 see PSS62)* £30
— Proof in gold *FDC* (Edition: 500 see PGC4P) * £600

H19

H19 **Fifty pence.** 250th Anniversary of the foundation of the Royal Botanical Gardens, Kew.
R. A design showing the pagoda, a building associated with the Royal Botanical Gardens
at Kew, encircled by a vine and accompanied by the dates '1759' and '2009', with the
word 'KEW' at the base of the pagoda.(Reverse design: Christopher Le Brun)
2009..£3
— Specimen in presentation pack (Issued: 128,364)...£7
— Proof *FDC* (in 2009 set, see PS97)* £7
— Proof in silver *FDC* (Issued: 7,575)...£30
— Proof piedfort in silver *FDC* (Issued: 2,967))..£55
— Proof in gold *FDC* (Issued: 629)..£800
— Proof piedfort in gold *FDC* (see PG50PPCS)*..£1200
H20 **Fifty new pence.** R. Britannia (See H1).
2009
— Proof *FDC* (in 2009 set, see PS100)* £15
— Proof in silver *FDC* (in 2009 set, see PSS40)*...£30
— Proof in gold *FDC* (in 2009 set, see PG50PCS)* £600
— Proof piedfort in gold *FDC* (in 2009 set, see PG50PPCS)* £1200

Coins marked thus were originally issued in Royal Mint sets.

H21   **Fifty new pence.** Accession to European Economic Community R. Clasped hands. (See H2)
2009
— Proof *FDC* (in 2009 set, see PS100)* £15
— Proof in silver *FDC* (in 2009 set, see PSS40)* £30
— Proof in gold *FDC* (in 2009 set, see PG50PCS)* £600
— Proof piedfort in gold *FDC* (in 2009 set, see PG50PPCS)* £1200

H22   **Fifty pence.** R. Presidency of the Council of European Community Ministers and completion of the Single Market. R. Conference table top and twelve stars. (See 4352)
2009
— Proof *FDC* (in 2009 set, see PS100)* £15
— Proof in silver *FDC* (in 2009 set, see PSS40)* £30
— Proof in gold *FDC* (in 2009 set, see PG50PCS)* £600
— Proof piedfort in gold *FDC* (in 2009 set, see PG50PPCS)* £1200

H23   **Fifty pence.** 50th Anniversary of the Normandy Landings on D-Day. R. Allied Invasion Force (See 4353)
2009
— Proof *FDC* (in 2009 set, see PS100)* £15
— Proof in silver *FDC* (in 2009 set, see PSS40)* £30
— Proof in gold *FDC* (in 2009 set, see PG50PCS)* £600
— Proof piedfort in gold *FDC* (in 2009 set, see PG50PPCS)* £1200

H24   H25

H24   **Fifty pence.** 100th Anniversary of Girl Guides. R. A design which depicts a repeating pattern of the current identity of Girl Guiding, UK, accompanied by the inscription 'CELEBRATING ONE HUNDRED YEARS OF GIRLGUIDING UK' and the denomination 'FIFTY PENCE' (Reverse design: Jonathan Evans and Donna Hainan)
2010 ....£1
— Specimen on presentation card (Issued: 99,075)) £5
— Specimen in presentation folder (Edition: 50,000) £7
— Proof *FDC* (in 2010 set, see PS101)* £7
— Proof in silver *FDC* (Issued: 5,271))...£30
— Proof piedfort in silver *FDC* (Issued: 2,879) £55
— Proof in gold *FDC* (Issued: 355)..£600

H25   **Fifty pence.** Fifth Anniversary of the World Wildlife Fund. R. A design which features 50 different icons symbolising projects and programmes that the World   Wildlife Fund has supported over the course of the last 50 years, with the Panda logo of the organisation in the centre and the date '2011' below. (Reverse design: Matthew Dent)
2011 ....£1
— Specimen in presentation folder (Issued: 67,299) £7
— Proof *FDC* (in 2011 set, see PS104)...£7
— Proof in silver *FDC* (Issued: 24,870) £42
— Proof piedfort in silver *FDC* (Issued: 2,244)..£73
— Proof in gold *FDC* (Issued: 243)..£725

Coins marked thus were originally issued in Royal Mint sets.

H26   H27

H26   **Fifty pence.** R. A version of the Royal Arms with the inscription 'FIFTY PENCE' above and the denomination '50' below. (Reverse design: Christopher Ironside).
2013
- —   Specimen in presentation folder £8
- —   Proof *FDC* (in 2013 set, see PS109)* £5
- —   Proof silver *FDC* (Issued: 1,823) £45
- —   Proof piedfort in silver *FDC* (Issued: 816) £90
- —   Proof in gold *FDC*(Issued: 198) £600

H27   **Fifty pence.** Centenary of the birth of Benjamin Britten. R. In the centre the name 'BENJAMIN BRITTEN' superimposed over musical staves with the inscription 'BLOW BUGLE BLOW' above and 'SET THE WILD ECHOES FLYING' below. (Reverse design: Tom Phillips).
2013
- —   Specimen in presentation folder £8
- —   Proof silver *FDC* (Issued: 717) £45
- —   Proof piedfort in silver *FDC* (Issued: 515) £90
- —   Proof in gold *FDC*(Issued: 70) £800

H28   H29

H28   **Fifty pence**. Commonwealth Games R. A design of a cyclist and a sprinter with the Scottish Saltire bisecting the coin and the inscription 'XX COMMONWEALTH GAMES GLASGOW' and the date'2014' (Reverse design: Alex Loudon with Dan Flashman).
2014
- —   Specimen in presentation folder £10
- —   Proof *FDC* (in 2014 set, see PS112)* £5
- —   Proof silver *FDC* (Edition: 4,500 including coins in sets) £45
- —   Proof piedfort in silver *FDC* (Edition: 3,513 including coins in sets) £90
- —   Proof in gold *FDC* (Edition: 450) £800

H29   **Fifty pence.** Battle of Britain commemorative. R. A design showing airmen running to their planes with enemy aircraft overhead with the inscription 'THE BATTLE OF BRITAIN 1940' (Reverse design: Gary Breeze).
2015
- —   BU in presentation folder £8
- —   Proof *FDC* (in 2015 set, see PS116)* £5
- —   Proof in silver *FDC* (Edition: 3,000 see PSS63 and PSS64) £50
- —   Proof piedfort in silver *FDC* (Edition: 1,500 see PSS65) £100
- —   Proof in gold *FDC* (Edition: 500 see PGC4P)) £675

* *Coins marked thus were originally issued in Royal Mint sets.*

Obverse portrait by Jody Clark

H30   H31

H30 **Fifty pence.**
2015
—   Proof *FDC* (in 2015 set, see PS116)*...
—   Proof in silver *FDC* (Edition: 7,500 see PSS63)*
—   Proof in gold *FDC* (Edition: 500 see PGC5P)*
2016
—   Proof *FDC* (in 2016 set, see PSS119)*
—   Proof in silver *FDC* (Edition: 1,500 see PSS68)*

H31 **Fifty pence.** Battle of Britain commemorative. R.A design showing airmen running to their planes with enemy aircraft overhead with the inscription 'THE BATTLE OF BRITAIN 1940' (Reverse design: Gary Breeze).
2015
—   Proof in silver *FDC* (Edition: 4,200)...£50
—   Proof piedfort in silver *FDC* (Edition: 1,940) £100
—   Proof in gold *FDC* (Edition: 520)..£675

H32

H32 **Fifty pence.** Nine hundred and fiftieth anniversary of the Battle of Hastings. R. A design showing the scene from the Bayeux tapestry depicting King Harold with an arrow in his eye accompanied by the inscription 'BATTLE OF HASTINGS 1066'and the date of the year. (Reverse design John Bergdahl).
2016
—   Specimen in presentation folder £10
—   Proof *FDC* (in 2016 set, see PS119)*...£15
—   Proof in silver *FDC* (Edition: 6,000)...£50
—   Proof piedfort in silver *FDC* (Edition : 3,000) £100
—   Proof in gold *FDC* (Edition : 500)..£755

* *Coins marked thus were originally issued in Royal Mint sets.*

H33

H33 **Fifty pence.** One hundred and fiftieth anniversary of the birth of Beatrix Potter. R. A silhouette of Beatrix Potter accompanied by an image of Peter Rabbit surrounded by a floral motif with the inscription 'BEATRIX POTTER 1866 1943'. (Reverse design: Emma Noble)

2016
— Specimen in presentation folder £10
— Proof in silver *FDC* (Edition: 7,750)...£55
— Proof piedfort in silver *FDC* (Edition : 2,500)..£100
— Proof in gold *FDC* (Edition : 750)... £675

H34   H35

H34 **Fifty pence.** One hundred and fiftieth anniversary of the birth of Beatrix Potter. R. A portrait of Peter Rabbit with the inscription 'PETER RABBIT'. (Reverse design: Emma Noble)

2016
— Specimen in presentation folder...£10
— Proof in silver *FDC* with colour (Edition: 15,000) £55
— Proof piedfort in silver *FDC* (Edition : 2,500)...£100

H35 **Fifty pence.** One hundred and fiftieth anniversary of the birth of Beatrix Potter. R. A portrait of Jemima Puddle-Duck with the inscription 'JEMIMA PUDDLE-DUCK'. (Reverse design: Emma Noble)

2016
— Specimen in presentation folder...£10
— Proof in silver *FDC* (Edition: 15,000)...£55
— Proof piedfort in silver *FDC* (Edition : 2,500) £100

H36   H37

H36 **Fifty pence.** One hundred and fiftieth anniversary of the birth of Beatrix Potter. R.A portrait of Squirrel Nutkin with the inscription 'SQUIRREL NUTKIN' (Reverse design; Emma Noble)
2016
— Specimen in presentation folder..£10
— Proof in silver *FDC* with colour (Edition: 15,000)...£55

H37 **Fifty pence.** One hundred and fiftieth anniversary of the birth of Beatrix Potter. R.A portrait of Mrs Tiggy-Winkle with the inscription 'MRS TIGGY-WINKLE'. (Reverse design: Emma Noble)
2016
— Specimen in presentation folder..£10
— Proof in silver *FDC* with colour (Edition: 15,000)...£55

H38

H38 **Fifty pence.** Team GB R. A depiction of a swimmer with the Team GB logo, the Olympic rings and the inscription 'TEAM GB' (Reverse design: Consultancy Uniform)
2016
— Specimen in presentation folder..£5
— Proof in silver *FDC* (Edition: 4,000)..£50
— Proof piedfort in silver *FDC* (Edition :2,016)...£100
— Proof in gold *FDC* (Edition : 306)...£725

NICKEL-BRASS

ONE POUND COINS
Obverse portrait by Arnold Machin

J1   J2

J1   **One pound.** R. The Ensigns Armorial of Our United Kingdom of Great Britain and Northern Ireland with the value 'ONE POUND' below and the edge inscription 'DECUS ET TUTAMEN' (Reverse design: Eric Sewell)

1983..£5
—   Specimen in presentation folder (Issued: 484,900).......................................£5
—   Proof *FDC* (in 1983 set, seePS33)*...£5
—   Proof in silver *FDC* (Issued: 50,000)..£35
—   Proof piedfort in silver *FDC* (Issued: 10,000) £125

J2   **One pound.** (Scottish design). R. A thistle eradicated enfiling a representation of Our Royal Diadem with the value 'ONE POUND' below and the edge inscription 'NEMO ME IMPUNE LACESSIT' (Reverse design: Leslie Durbin)

1984..£5
—   Specimen in presentation folder (Issued: 27,960).....................................£5
—   Proof *FDC* (in 1984 set, see PS34)*...£5
—   Proof in silver *FDC* (Issued: 44,855)..£30
—   Proof piedfort in silver *FDC* (Issued: 15,000) £60

Obverse portrait by Raphael Maklouf

J3

J3   **One pound** (Welsh design). R. A leek eradicated enfiling a representation of Our Royal Diadem with the value 'ONE POUND' below and the edge inscription 'PLEIDIOL WYF I'M GWLAD". (Reverse design: Leslie Durbin)

1985..£4
—   Specimen in presentation folder (Issued: 24,850).....................................£4
—   Proof *FDC* (in 1985 set, see PS35)*...£5
—   Proof in silver *FDC* (Issued: 50,000)..£30
—   Proof piedfort in silver *FDC* (Issued: 15,000) £60
1990..£5
—   Proof *FDC* (in 1990 set, see PS45)*...£6
—   Proof in silver *FDC* (Issued: 23,277)..£28

* Coins marked thus were originally issued in Royal Mint sets.

J4   J5

J4 **One pound** (Northern Irish design). R. A flax plant eradicated enfiling a representation
of Our Royal Diadem with value 'ONE POUND' below and the edge inscription
'DECUS ET TUTAMEN'. (Reverse design: Leslie Durbin)
1986..£5
— Specimen in presentation folder (Issued: 19,908)..£5
— Proof *FDC* (in 1986 set, see PS37)*..£4
— Proof in silver *FDC* (Issued: 37, 958)...£30
— Proof piedfort in silver *FDC* (Issued: 15,000) £60
1991..£5
— Proof *FDC* (in 1991 set, see PS47)*..£6
— Proof in silver *FDC* (Issued: 22,922)..£28

J5 **One pound** (English design). R. An oak tree enfiling a representation of Our Royal
Diadem with the value 'ONE POUND' below and the edge inscription 'DECUS ET
TUTAMEN'. (Reverse design: Leslie Durbin)
1987..£4
— Specimen in presentation folder (Issued: 72,607)..£4
— Proof *FDC* (in 1987 set, see PS39)*..£6
— Proof in silver *FDC* (Issued: 50,000)...£30
— Proof piedfort in silver *FDC* (Issued: 15,000) £60
1992..£5
— Proof *FDC* (in 1992 set, see PS49)*..£6
— Proof in silver *FDC* (Issued: 13,065)...£30

J6 **One pound** (Royal Shield). R. A Shield of Our Royal Arms ensigned by a representation
of Our Royal Crown with the value 'ONE POUND' below and the Edge inscription
'DECUS ET TUTAMEN'. (Reverse design: Derek Gorringe)
1988..£5
— Specimen in presentation folder (Issued: 29,550)..£6
— Proof *FDC* (in 1988 set, see PS41)*..£6
— Proof in silver *FDC* (Issued: 50,000)...£35
— Proof piedfort in silver *FDC* (Issued: 10,000) £60

J7 **One pound** (Scottish design). Edge 'NEMO ME IMPUNE LACESSIT' (Illus. as J2)
1989..£5
— Proof *FDC* (in 1989 set, see PS43)*..£6
— Proof in silver *FDC* (Issued: 22,275)...£30
— Proof piedfort in silver *FDC* (Issued: 10,000) £60

J8 **One pound** (Royal Arms design). Edge 'DECUS ET TUTAMEN' (Illus. as J1)
1993..£5
— Proof *FDC* (in 1993 set, see PS51)*..£6
— Proof in silver *FDC* (Issued: 16,526)...£30
— Proof piedfort in silver *FDC* (Issued: 12,500) £60

* Coins marked thus were originally issued in Royal Mint sets.

J9 **One pound** (Scottish design). R: A Lion rampant within a double tressure flory counter-flory, being that quartering of Our Royal Arms known heraldically as Scotland with the value 'ONE POUND' below and the edge inscription 'NEMO ME IMPUNE LACESSIT'. (Reverse design: Norman Sillman)

1994..£4
— Specimen in presentation folder..£5
— Proof *FDC* (in 1994 set, see PS53)* £6
— Proof in silver *FDC* (Issued: 25,000)...£30
— Proof piedfort in silver *FDC* (Issued: 11,722) £60

J10 **One pound** (Welsh design). R. A dragon passant, being Our badge for Wales with the value 'ONE POUND' below and the edge inscription 'PLEIDIOL WYF I'M GWLAD'. (Reverse design: Norman Sillman)

1995..£4
— Specimen in presentation folder, English version £5
— Specimen in presentation folder, Welsh version £10
— Proof *FDC* (in 1995 set, see PS55)* £5
— Proof in silver *FDC* (Issued: 27,445)..£30
— Proof piedfort in silver *FDC* (Issued: 8,458) £70

J11 **One pound** (Northern Irish design). R. A Celtic cross charged at the centre with an Annulet therein a Pimpernel flower and overall an ancient Torque, symbolizing that part of Our Kingdom known as Northern Ireland with the value 'ONE POUND' below and the edge inscription 'DECUS ET TUTAMEN'. (Reverse design: Norman Sillman)

1996..£4
— Specimen in presentation folder..£6
— Proof *FDC* (in 1996 set, see PS57)* £6
— Proof in silver *FDC* (Issued: 25,000)..£30
— Proof piedfort in silver *FDC* (Issued: 10,000.. £60

J12

J12 **One pound** (English design) R. Three lions passant guardant, being that quartering of Our Royal Arms known heraldically as *England*, with the value 'ONE POUND' below and the edge inscription 'DECUS ET TUTAMEN.(Reverse design: Norman Sillman)

1997..£4
— Specimen in presentation folder (Issued 56,996)...£5
— Proof *FDC* (in 1997 set, see PS59)* £5
— Proof in silver *FDC* (Issued: 20,137)..£30
— Proof piedfort in silver *FDC* (Issued: 10,000) £60

* Coins marked thus were originally issued in Royal Mint sets.

Obverse portrait by Ian Rank-Broadley

J13

J13   **One pound** (Royal Arms design). Edge: 'DECUS ET TUTAMEN' (rev. as J1)

1998 ....£5
—   Proof *FDC* (in 1998 set, see PS61)* £6
—   Proof in silver *FDC* (Issued: 13,863) £30
—   Proof piedfort in silver *FDC* (Issued: 7,894) £60

2003 ....£3
—   Specimen in presentation folder (Issued: 23,760)...£5
—   Proof *FDC* (in 2003 set, see PS78)* £6
—   Proof in silver *FDC* (Issued: 15,830)..£30
—   Proof piedfort in silver *FDC* (Issued: 9,871) £60

2008
—   Specimen in presentation folder (Issued: 18,336)...£7
—   Proof *FDC* (in 2008 set, see PS93)* £6
—   Proof in silver *FDC* (Issued: 8,441)..£30
—   Proof in gold *FDC* (Issued: 674)..£800
—   Proof in platinum *FDC* (in 2008 set, see PPEBCS)*..£800

2013. 30th Anniversary of the introduction of the £1 coin
—   Proof silver *FDC* (Issued: 1,311 in 3 coin sets, see PSS55)*...............................£60
—   Proof in gold *FDC* (Issued: 17 in 3 coin sets, see PG31S)* £1500

J13A 2008
—   Proof in silver with selected gold plating on reverse *FDC* (in 2008 set,
see PSS30)*..£40

J14   **One pound.** (Scottish lion design). Edge: 'NEMO ME IMPUNE LACESSIT'

1999 ....£3
—   Specimen in presentation folder...£5
—   Proof *FDC* (in 1999 set, see PS63)* £6
—   Proof in silver *FDC* (Issued: 16,328)..£30
—   Proof piedfort in silver *FDC* (Issued: 9,975) £60

2008
—   Proof in gold *FDC* (in 2008 set, see PG1PCS)* £600

J14A 1999
—   Proof in silver *FDC,* with reverse frosting, (Issued: 1,994)*...................................£50

J14B 2008
—   Proof in silver with selected gold plating on reverse *FDC* (in 2008 set, see PSS30)*.....£40

J15   **One pound.** (Welsh design). Edge: 'PLEIDIOL WYF I'M GWLAD'

2000..£3
—   Proof *FDC* (in 2000 set, see PS65)* £6
—   Proof in silver *FDC* (Issued: 15,913)..£30
—   Proof piedfort in silver *FDC* (Issued: 9,994) £60

2008
—   Proof in gold *FDC* (in 2008 set, see PG1PCS)* £600

J15A 2000
—   Proof in silver *FDC,* with reverse frosting, (Issued: 1,994)*...................................£50

* Coins marked thus were originally issued in Royal Mint sets.

J15B 2008
— Proof in silver with selected gold plating on reverse *FDC* (in 2008 set,
see PSS30)* £40
J16 **One pound.** (Northern Irish design). Edge: 'DECUS ET TUTAMEN'
2001...£3
— Proof *FDC* (in 2001 set, see PS68)* £6
— Proof in silver *FDC* (Issued: 11,697)..£30
— Proof piedfort in silver *FDC* (Issued: 8,464) £60
2008
— Proof in gold *FDC* (in 2008 set, see PG1PCS)* £800
J16A 2001
— Proof in silver *FDC*, with reverse frosting, (Issued: 1,540)*..................£60
J16B 2008
— Proof in silver with selected gold plating on reverse *FDC* (in 2008 set, see PSS30)* £40
J17 **One pound.** (English design) Edge: 'DECUS ET TUTAMEN' (rev. as J12)
2002...£3
— Proof *FDC* (in 2002 set, see PS72)* £6
— Proof in silver *FDC* (Issued: 17,693)..£30
— Proof piedfort in silver *FDC* (Issued: 6,599) £60
— Proof in gold *FDC* (in 2002 set, see PGJS1)*.......................................£800
2008
— Proof in gold *FDC* (in 2008 set, see PG1PCS)* £800
J17A 2002
— Proof in silver *FDC*, with reverse frosting, (Issued: 1,540)*..................£60
J17B 2008
— Proof in silver with selected gold plating on reverse *FDC* (in 2008 set,
see PSS30)* £40

J18

J18 **One pound.** Scotland R. A representation of the Forth Railway Bridge with a border of
railway tracks and beneath, the value 'ONE POUND' and an incuse decorative feature
on the edge symbolising bridges and pathways. (Reverse design: Edwina Ellis)
2004...£3
— Specimen in presentation folder (Issued: 24,014)...................................£5
— Proof *FDC* (in 2004 set, see PS81)* £6
— Proof in silver *FDC* (Issued: 11,470) £30
— Proof piedfort in silver *FDC* (Issued: 7,013) £60
— Proof in gold *FDC* (Issued: 2,618)..£800
2008
— Proof in gold *FDC* (in 2008 set, see PG1PCS)* £800
J18A **One pound pattern.** Scotland. R. Forth Railway Bridge but dated 2003 with plain edge
and hallmark, reading "PATTERN" instead of "ONE POUND"
— Proof in silver *FDC* (in 2003 set, see PPS1)*...£25
— Proof in gold *FDC* (in 2003 set, see PPS2)*...£750

* *Coins marked thus were originally issued in Royal Mint sets.*

| J18B | J19 | J19B | J20 |

J18B One pound pattern. Scotland. R. Unicorn with the word "Pattern" below with plain
edge and hallmark and dated 2004. (Reverse design: Timothy Noad)
— Proof in silver *FDC* (in 2004 set, see PPS3)* £25
— Proof in gold *FDC* (in 2004 set, see PPS4)* £750

J18C 2008
— Proof in silver as 4595 with selected gold plating on reverse *FDC* (in 2008 set, see
PSS30)* £40

J19 One pound. Wales. R. A representation of the Menai Straits Bridge with a border of
railings and stanchions, the value 'ONE POUND' and an incuse decorative feature on the
edge symbolising bridges and pathways. (Reverse design: Edwina Ellis)
2005 ....£3
— Specimen in presentation folder (Issued: 24,802) £6
— Proof *FDC* (in 2005 set, see PS84)* £6
— Proof in silver *FDC* (Issued: 8,371) £35
— Proof piedfort in silver *FDC* (Issued: 6,007) £60
— Proof in gold *FDC* (Issued: 1,195) £800
2008
— Proof in gold *FDC* (in 2008 set, see PG1PCS)* £800

J19A One pound pattern. Wales. R. Menai Straits Bridge but dated 2003 with plain edge and
hallmark
— Proof in silver *FDC* (in 2003 set, see PPS1)* £25
— Proof in gold *FDC* (in 2003 set, see PPS2)* £750

J19B One pound pattern. Wales. R Dragon and the word "Pattern" below with plain edge and
hallmark and dated 2004. (Reverse design: Timothy Noad)
— Proof in silver *FDC* (in 2004 set, see PPS3)* £25
— Proof in gold *FDC* (in 2004 set, see PPS4)* £750

J19C 2008
— Proof in silver as J19 with selected gold plating on reverse *FDC* (in 2008 set,
see PSS30)* £40

J20 One pound. Northern Ireland. R. A representation of the Egyptian Arch Railway Bridge
in County Down with a border of railway station canopy dags, the value 'ONE POUND'
and an incuse decorative feature on the edge symbolising bridges and pathways. (Reverse
design: Edwina Ellis)
2006 ....£4
— Specimen in presentation folder £6
— Proof *FDC* (in 2006 set, see PS87)* £8
— Proof in silver *FDC* (Edition: 20,000) £30
— Proof piedfort in silver *FDC* (Edition: 7,500) £60
— Proof in gold *FDC* (Edition: 1,500) £800
2008
— Proof in gold *FDC* (in 2008 set, see PG1PCS)* £800

J20A One pound pattern. Northern Ireland. R. MacNeill's Egyptian Arch Railway Bridge but
dated 2003 with plain edge and hallmark
— Proof in silver *FDC* (in 2003 set, see PPS1)* £25
— Proof in gold *FDC* (in 2003 set, see PPS2)* £750

* Coins marked thus were originally issued in Royal Mint sets.

J20B   J21   J21A   J21B

J20B **One pound pattern.** Northern Ireland. ℞ Stag and the word 'Pattern' below with plain
edge and hallmark and dated 2004. (Reverse design: Timothy Noad)
— Proof in silver *FDC* (in 2004 set, see PPS3)*..£25
— Proof in gold *FDC* (in 2004 set, see PPS4)*...£750
J20C 2008
— Proof in silver as J20 with selected gold plating on reverse *FDC* (in 2008 set,
see PSS30)* £40
J21 **One pound. England.** ℞. A representation of the Gateshead Millennium Bridge with a
border of struts, the value 'ONE POUND' and an incuse decorative feature on the edge
symbolising bridges and pathways. (Reverse design: Edwina Ellis)
2007...£4
— Specimen in presentation folder..£7
— Proof *FDC** (in 2007 set, see PS90) £8
— Proof in silver *FDC* (Issued: 10,110) £30
— Proof piedfort in silver *FDC* (Issued: 5,739) £60
— Proof in gold *FDC* (Issued: 1,112)..£800
2008
— Proof in gold *FDC* (in 2008 set, see PG1PCS)*...£800
J21A **One pound pattern.** England. ℞. Millennium Bridge but dated 2003 with plain edge and
hallmark
— Proof in silver *FDC* (in 2003 set, see PSS1)*...£25
— Proof in gold *FDC* (in 2003 set, see PPS2)*...£750
J21B **One pound pattern.** England. ℞. Lion with the word 'Pattern' below with plain edge and
hallmark and dated 2004. (Reverse design: Timothy Noad)
— Proof in silver *FDC* (in 2004 set, see PPS3)*...£25
— Proof in gold *FDC* (in 2004 set, see PPS4)*...£750
J21C 2008
— Proof in silver as J21 with selected gold plating on reverse *FDC* (in 2008 set,
see PSS30)* £40
J22 **One pound.** (Scottish design). Edge 'NEMO ME IMPUNE LACESSIT' (rev. as J2)
2008
— Proof in gold *FDC* (in 2008 set, see PG1PCS)*...£800
J22A 2008
— Proof in silver with selected gold plating on reverse *FDC* (in 2008 set,
see PSS30)*..£40
J23 **One pound.** (Welsh design). Edge 'PLEIDOL WYF I'M GWLAD' (rev. see J3)
2008
— Proof in gold *FDC* (in 2008 set, see PG1PCS)*...£800
J23A 2008
— Proof in silver with selected gold plating on reverse *FDC* (in 2008 set,
see PSS30)* £40
J24 **One pound.** (Northern Irish design). Edge 'DECUS ET TUTAMEN' (rev. see J4)
2008
— Proof in gold *FDC* (in 2008 set, see PG1PCS)*...£800

* *Coins marked thus were originally issued in Royal Mint sets.*

J24A 2008
— Proof in silver with selected gold plating on reverse *FDC* (in 2008 set, see PSS30)* £40

J25 **One pound.** (English design). Edge 'DECUS ET TUTAMEN' (rev. see J5)
2008
— Proof in gold *FDC* (in 2008 set, see PG1PCS)* £800

J25A 2008
— Proof in silver with selected gold plating on reverse *FDC* (in 2008 set, see PSS30)* £40

J26 **One pound.** (Royal Shield). Edge 'DECUS ET TUTAMEN'.
2008
— Proof in gold *FDC* (in 2008 set, see PG1PCS)* £800
2013. 30th Anniversary of the introduction of the £1 coin.
— Proof silver *FDC* (Issued: 1,311 in 3 coin sets, see PSS55)* £60
— Proof in gold *FDC* (Issued: 17 in 3 coin sets, see PG31S)* £1500

J26A 2008
— Proof in silver with selected gold plating on reverse FDC (in 2008 set, see PSS30)* £40

J27

J27 **One pound.** R. A shield of Our Royal Arms with the words 'ONE' to the left and 'POUND' to the right and the edge inscription 'DECUS ET TUTAMEN' (Reverse design: Matthew Dent)
2008 .... £3
— Proof *FDC* (in 2008 set, see PS96)* £5
— Proof in silver *FDC* (Issued: 5,000) £30
— Proof piedfort in silver *FDC* (Edition: 8,000) £50
— Proof in gold *FDC* (Issued: 860)* £800
— Proof in platinum *FDC* (in 2008 set, see PPRSAS)* £800
2009 .... £3
— Specimen in presentation folder (Edition: 15,000) £7
— Proof *FDC* (in 2009 set, see PS97)* £5
— BU in silver (Edition: 50,000) £30
— Proof in silver *FDC* (Edition: 20,000 including coins in sets) £35
— Proof in gold *FDC* (Edition: 1,000) £800
2010 .... £3
— Proof *FDC* (in 2010 set, see PS101)* £5
— BU in silver (Edition: 50,000) £30
— Proof in silver *FDC (*Edition: 20,000 including coins in sets) £35
2011 .... £3
— Proof *FDC* (in 2011 set, see PS104) * £5
— BU in silver £30
— Proof in silver *FDC* (in 2011 set, Edition: 2,500, see PSS44) * £35

* Coins marked thus were originally issued in Royal Mint sets.

2012..£3
—   Proof *FDC* (in 2012 set, see PS107)*...£3
—   BU in silver £25
—   Proof in silver with selected gold plating *FDC* (Edition: 2,012, see PSS48)* £40
—   Proof in gold *FDC* (Edition: 150 see PGDJS)*..£800
2013.. £3
—   Proof *FDC* (in 2013 set, see PS109) *... £7
—   BU in silver £25
—   Proof in silver *FDC* (Issued: 2296 including coins in sets) £40
—   Proof in gold *FDC* (Issued: 76 including coins in sets, see PGCAS)*.............£1000
2014..£3
—   Proof *FDC* (in 2014 set, see PS112) *...£3
—   BU in silver...£25
—   Proof in silver *FDC* (Edition: 2,014 see PSS56) *.......................................£35
2015
—   Proof *FDC* (in 2015 set, see PS115) *...£5
—   Proof in silver *FDC* (Edition: 7,500 see PSS61)*..£35
—   Proof in gold *FDC* (Edition: 500 see PGC4P) *.. £800
2016
—   BU (in 2016 set, see US57)
—   Proof *FDC* (in 2016 set, see PS119)*
—   Proof in silver *FDC* (Edition: 1,500 in sets, see PSS68)*

J28   J29

J28 – One pound. London. R. A design which depicts the official badges of the capital
cities of the United Kingdom, with the badge of London being the principal focus,
accompanied by the name 'LONDON' and the denomination 'ONE POUND' with the
edge inscription 'DOMINE DIRIGE NOS'. (Reverse design: Stuart Devlin)
2010..£3
—   Specimen on presentation card (Issued: 66,313)..£5
—   Specimen in presentation folder with J29 (Edition: 10,000)................................£14
—   Proof *FDC* (in 2010 set, see PS101)* £5
—   Proof in silver *FDC* (Issued: 7,693)..£35
—   Proof piedfort in silver *FDC* (Issued: 3,682) £55
—   Proof in gold *FDC* (Issued: 950)..£800
J29 – One pound. Belfast. R. A design which depicts the official badges of the capital cities of
the United Kingdom, with the badge of Belfast being the principal focus, accompanied
by the name 'BELFAST' and the denomination 'ONE POUND' with the edge inscription
'PRO TANTO QUID RETRIBUAMUS' (Reverse design: Stuart Devlin)
2010..£3
—   Specimen on presentation card (Issued: 64,461)..£5
—   Specimen in presentation folder with J28 (Edition: 10,000)................................£14
—   Proof *FDC* (in 2010 set, see PS101)* £5
—   Proof in silver *FDC* (Issued: 5,805)..£35
—   Proof piedfort in silver *FDC* (Issued: 3,503) £55
—   Proof in gold *FDC* (Issued: 585)..£800

* Coins marked thus were originally issued in Royal Mint sets.

J30   J31

J30   **One pound. Edinburgh.** R. A design which depicts the official badges of the capital
cities of the United Kingdom, with the badge of Edinburgh being the principal focus,
accompanied by the name 'EDINBURGH' and the denomination 'ONE POUND' with
the edge inscription 'NISI DOMINUS'. (Reverse design: Stuart Devlin)
2011 ....£3
—   Specimen in presentation folder with J31 (Edition: 10,000) £14
—   Proof *FDC* (in 2011 set, see PS104)*...£8
—   Proof in silver *FDC* (Issued: 4,973) £45
—   Proof piedfort in silver *FDC* (Issued: 2,696)..£78
—   Proof in gold *FDC* (Issued: 499) £950

J31   **One pound. Cardiff.** R. A design which depicts the official badges of the capital cities
of the United Kingdom, with the badge of Cardiff being the principal focus, accompanied
by the name 'CARDIFF' and the denomination 'ONE POUND' with the edge inscription
'Y DDRAIG GOCH DDYRY CYCHWYN ' (Reverse design: Stuart Devlin)
2011 ....£3
—   Specimen in presentation folder with J30 (Edition: 10,000)..................................£14
—   Proof *FDC* (in 2011 set, see PS104) *..£8
—   Proof in silver *FDC* (Issued: 5,553) £45
—   Proof piedfort in silver *FDC* (Issued: 1,615)..£78
—   Proof in gold *FDC* (Issued: 524) £950

J32   J33

J32   **One pound. England.** R. Depicts an oak branch paired with a Tudor-inspired rose
with the denomination 'ONE POUND' below and the edge inscription 'DECUS ET
TUTAMEN'. (Reverse design: Timothy Noad)
2013 ....£3
—   Specimen in presentation folder with J33...£18
—   Proof *FDC* (in 2013 set, see PS109) *..£7
—   Proof in silver *FDC* (Issued: 1,858) £50
—   Proof piedfort in silver *FDC* ((Issued: 1,071) £100
—   Proof in gold *FDC* ((Issued: 185)..£1000

J33   **One pound. Wales.** R. Depicts a leek and a daffodil with their leaves entwined and the
denomination 'ONE POUND' below and the edge inscription 'PLEIDIOL WYF I'M
GWLAD'. (Reverse design: Timothy Noad)
2013 ....£3
—   Specimen in presentation folder with J32...£18
—   Proof *FDC* (in 2013 set, see PS109) *..£7
—   Proof in silver *FDC* ((Issued: 1,618)...£50
—   Proof piedfort in silver *FDC* ((Issued: 860) £100
—   Proof in gold *FDC* ((Issued: 175)..£1000

* Coins marked thus were originally issued in Royal Mint sets.

J34   J35

J34 **One pound. Northern Ireland.** R. Depicts a flax and shamrock being the principle
focus for Northern Ireland accompanied by the denomination 'ONE POUND' and
the edge inscription 'DECUS ET TUTANEM. (Reverse design: Timothy Noad)
2014 ....£3
— Specimen in presentation folder with J35..£18
— Proof *FDC* (in 2014 set, see PS112)*..£7
— Proof in silver *FDC* (Edition: 6,028 including coins in sets) £50
— Proof piedfort in silver *FDC* (Edition: 3,014 including coins in sets) £100
— Proof in gold *FDC* (Edition: 560 including coins in sets)................................£1000

J35 **One pound. Scotland.** R. Depicts the thistle and bluebell being the principle focus for
Scotland accompanied by the denomination 'ONE POUND' and the edge inscription
'NEMO ME IMPUNE LACESSIT'. (Reverse design: Timothy Noad)
2014 ....£3
— Specimen in presentation folder with J34..£18
— Proof *FDC* (in 2014 set, see PS112)*..£7
— Proof in silver *FDC* (Edition: 6,028 including coins in sets) £50
— Proof piedfort in silver *FDC* (Edition: 3,014 including coins in sets) £100
— Proof in gold *FDC* (Edition: 560 including coins in sets)................................£1000

Obverse portrait by Jody Clark

J37

J36 **One pound.** R. A shield of Our Royal Arms with the words 'ONE' to the left and
'POUND' to the right and the edge inscription 'DECUS ET TUTAMEN'
(Reverse design: Matthew Dent)
2015
— Proof *FDC* (in 2015 set, see PS116) *..£5
— Proof in silver *FDC* (Edition: 7,500 see PSS63)*
— Proof in gold *FDC* (Edition: 500 see PGC5P) *

J37 **One Pound.** R. A depiction of Our Royal Arms accompanied by the inscription 'ONE
POUND' below with the edge inscription 'DECUS ET TUTAMEN' (Reverse design:
Timothy Noad)
2015
— BU in presentation pack £10
— Proof in silver *FDC* (Edition: 3,500)..£50
— Proof piedfort in silver *FDC* (Edition: 2,000) £100
— Proof in gold *FDC* (Edition: 500)..£850

* *Coins marked thus were originally issued in Royal Mint sets.*

J38

J38 **One Pound.** R. A design depicting a lion, unicorn, stag and dragon surrounding a crown accompanied by the denomination 'ONE POUND' with the edge inscription 'DECUS ET TUTAMEN'. (Reverse design: Gregory Cameron).

2016
- — Specimen in presentation folder £10
- — Proof *FDC* (in 2016 set, see PS119)*
- — Proof in silver *FDC* (Edition: 7,500)..£50
- — Proof piedfort in silver *FDC* (Edition: 3,000) £100
- — Proof in gold *FDC* (Edition: 500)...   £895

NICKEL-BRASS

TWO POUND COINS
Obverse portrait by Raphael Maklouf

K1

K1 **Two pounds.** R. St. Andrew's cross with a crown of laurel leaves and surmounted by a thistle of Scotland with date '1986' above. Edge 'XIII COMMONWEALTH GAMES SCOTLAND' (Reverse design: Norman Sillman)

1986...£5
- — Specimen in presentation folder...£8
- — Proof *FDC** (in 1986 set, see PS37)* £10
- — 500 silver (Issued: 58,881)...£18
- — Proof in silver *FDC* (Issued: 59,779)...£35
- — Proof in gold *FDC* (Issued: 3,277)...£750

* Coins marked thus were originally issued in Royal Mint sets.

K2   K3   K4

K2   **Two pounds** 300th Anniversary of Bill of Rights. ℞ Cypher of W&M (King William and Queen Mary) interlaced surmounting a horizontal Parliamentary mace and a representation of the Royal Crown above and the dates '1689'and '1989' below, all within the inscription 'TERCENTENARY OF THE BILL OF RIGHTS'. (Reverse design: John Lobban)

1989..£5
— Specimen in presentation folder...£8
— Proof *FDC* (in 1989 set, see PS43)* £10
— Proof in silver *FDC* (Issued: 25,000)..£35
— Proof piedfort in silver *FDC* (in 1989 set, seePSS01)* £60

K3   **Two pounds** 300th Anniversary of Claim of Right (Scotland). ℞. As 4312, but with Crown of Scotland and the inscription 'TERCENTENARY OF THE CLAIM OF RIGHT'. (Reverse design: John Lobban)

1989..£15
— Specimen in presentation folder..£20
— Proof *FDC* (in 1989 set, see PS43)* £15
— Proof in silver *FDC* (Issued: 24,852)..£35
— Proof piedfort in silver *FDC* (in 1989 set, seePSS01)* £60

K4   **Two pounds** 300th Anniversary of the Bank of England. ℞: Bank's original Corporate Seal, with Crown & Cyphers of William III & Mary II and the dates '1694' and '1994'. Edge 'SIC VOS NON VOBIS'on the silver and base metal versions. (Reverse design: Leslie Durbin)

1994..£5
— Specimen in presentation folder...£8
— Proof *FDC* (in 1994 set, see PS53)* £10
— Proof in silver *FDC* (Issued: 27, 957)..£35
— Proof piedfort in silver *FDC* (Issued: 9,569) £60
— Proof in gold *FDC* (Issued: 1,000)..£750

K4A **— Gold Error – known as a Mule coin.** £2500

The obverse of the 1994 Bank of England issue should have included the denomination 'TWO POUNDS' as this was not included in the design of the commemorative reverse. An unknown number of coins were struck and issued in gold using the die that was reserved for the Double Sovereign or Two Pound coins in the sovereign series. The Royal Mint wrote to its retail customers inviting them to return the error coin for replacement with the correct design. No details are known as to how many were returned, nor how many exist in the market. The incorrect obverse can be seen at SD2 in the section listing Gold Sovereigns; the correct obverse is at K1.

* Coins marked thus were originally issued in Royal Mint sets.

K5   K6

K5   **Two pounds** 50th Anniversary of the End of World War II. ℞: A stylised representation of a dove as the symbol of Peace. Edge '1945 IN PEACE GOODWILL 1995'. (Reverse design: John Mills)

1995..£5
—   Specimen in presentation folder..£8
—   Proof *FDC* (in 1995 set, see PS55)*..£10
—   Proof in silver *FDC* (Issued: 35,751)...£35
—   Proof piedfort in silver *FDC* (Edition: 10,000)..£60
—   Proof in gold *FDC* (Issued: 2,500)...£750

K6   **Two pounds** 50th Anniversary of the Establishment of the United Nations. ℞: 50th Anniversary symbol and a fanning pattern of flags with the inscription 'NATIONS UNITED FOR PEACE' above and the dates '1945-1995'below. (Reverse design: Michael Rizzello)

1995..£5
—   Specimen in presentation folder..£7
—   Specimen in card (issued as part of multi country United Nations Collection)..........£7
—   Proof in silver *FDC* (Edition: 175,000) £35
—   Proof piedfort in silver *FDC* (Edition: 10,000)...£60
—   Proof in gold *FDC* (Edition: 17,500)..£750

K7

K7   **Two pounds** European Football Championships. ℞: A stylised representation of a football with the date '1996' centrally placed and surrounded by sixteen small rings. Edge: 'TENTH EUROPEAN CHAMPIONSHIP'. The gold versions have a plain edge with no inscription. (Reverse design: John Mills)

1996..£6
—   Specimen in presentation folder..£8
—   Proof *FDC* (in 1996 set, see PS57)*..£10
—   Proof in silver *FDC* (Issued: 25,163)...£35
—   Proof piedfort in silver *FDC* (Issued: 7,634) £60
—   Proof in gold *FDC* (Issued: 2,098)...£750

K7A   **Incorrect blank.** When struck the coins have a dished appearance on both the obverse and reverse but several pieces in gold have been reported where the surface of the coins is flat. Enquiries at the Mint are continuing with a view to understanding how this could have occurred...£1500

* Coins marked thus were originally issued in Royal Mint sets.

Bimetallic issues

K8

K8 **Two pounds** Bimetallic currency issue. ℞. Four concentric circles representing the Iron Age, 18th Century industrial development, silicon chip, and Internet. Edge: 'STANDING ON THE SHOULDERS OF GIANTS'. (Reverse design: Bruce Rushin)

1997...£5
— Specimen in presentation folder...£8
— Proof *FDC* (in 1997 set, see PS59)*...£10
— Proof in silver *FDC* (Issued: 29,910)..£32
— Proof piedfort in silver *FDC* (Issued: 10,000) £60
— Proof in gold *FDC* (Issued: 2,482)...£750

Obverse portrait by Ian Rank-Broadley

K9

K9 **Two pounds.** Bimetallic currency issue. ℞. Four concentric circles, representing the Iron Age, 18th Century industrial development, silicon chip and Internet. Edge: 'STANDING ON THE SHOULDERS OF GIANTS'.

1998...£5
— Proof *FDC* (in 1998 set, see PS61)*...£10
— Proof in silver *FDC* (Issued: 19,978)..£32
— Proof piedfort in silver *FDC* (Issued: 7,646) £60
1999...£4
2000...£4
— Proof *FDC* (in 2000 set, see PS65)*...£10
— Proof in silver *FDC* (in 2000 set, see PSS10)*..£35
2001...£4
— Proof *FDC* (see PS68)*..£10
2002...£4
— Proof *FDC* (in 2002 set, see PS72)*...£10
— Proof in gold *FDC* (in 2002 set, see PGJS1)* £750
2003...£4
— Proof *FDC* (see PS78)*..£10
2004...£4
— Proof *FDC* (in 2004 set, see PS81)*...£10
2005...£4
— Proof *FDC* (see PS84)*..£10
2006...£4
— Proof *FDC* (in 2006 set, see PS87)*...£10
— Proof in silver *FDC* (in 2006 set, see PSS22)*..£35
2007...£4

* Coins marked thus were originally issued in Royal Mint sets.

2008..£4
— Proof *FDC* (in 2008 set, see PS93)*...£10
2009..£4
— Proof *FDC* (in 2009 set, see PS97)*...£10
— Proof in silver *FDC* (in 2009 set, see PSS37)*...£35
2010..£4
— Proof *FDC* (in 2010 set, see PS101)*...£10
— Proof in silver *FDC* (in 2010 set, see PSS41)*..£35
2011..£4
— Proof *FDC* (in 2010 set, see PS104)*...£10
— Proof in silver *FDC* (in 2010 set, see PSS44)*..£35
2012..£4
— Proof *FDC* (in 2012 set, see PS107)* £3
— Proof in silver *FDC* (Edition: 2,012, see PSS47)*.....................................£30
— Proof in gold *FDC* (Edition: 150 see PGDJS)* £800
2013..£4
— Proof *FDC* (in 2013 set, see PS109)* £5
— Proof in silver *FDC* (Edition: 2,013, see PSS50)*.....................................£30
— Proof in gold *FDC* (Edition: 50 see PGCAS)* £1000
 2014...£4
— Proof *FDC* (in 2014 set, see PS112)*...£5
— Proof in silver *FDC* (Edition: 2,014 see PSS56)*
2015.. £4
— Proof *FDC* (in 2015 set, see PS115) *...£5
— Proof in silver *FDC* (Edition: 9,000 see PSS62)*
— Proof in gold *FDC* (Edition: 500 see PGC4P) *

K10 **Two pounds.** Rugby World Cup. Ɽ. In the centre a rugby ball and goal posts surrounded by a stylised stadium with the denomination 'TWO POUNDS' and the date '1999'. Edge: 'RUGBY WORLD CUP 1999'. (Reverse design: Ron Dutton)

1999..£5
— Specimen in presentation folder...£8
— Proof *FDC* (in 1999 set, see PS63)*...£10
— Proof in silver *FDC* (Issued: 9,665)...£40
— Proof in gold *FDC* (Issued: 311)...£750

K10A   K11

K10A — Proof piedfort in silver with coloured hologram on reverse *FDC* (Issued: 10,000) ..£150

K11 **Two pounds.** Marconi commemorative. Ɽ. Decorative radio waves emanating from a spark of electricity linking the zeros of the date to represent the generation of the signal that crossed the Atlantic with the date '2001' and the denomination 'TWO POUNDS'. Edge: 'WIRELESS BRIDGES THE ATLANTIC MARCONI 1901'. (Reverse design: Robert Evans)

2001..£5
— Specimen in presentation folder...£7
— Proof *FDC* (in 2001 set, see PS68)*...£10
— Proof in silver *FDC* (Issued: 11,488)...£35
— Proof piedfort in silver *FDC* (Issued: 6,759) £60
— Proof in gold *FDC* (Issued: 1,658)...£750

K11A — Proof in silver *FDC*, with reverse frosting. (Issued: 4,803 in a 2-coin set with a Canadian $5 Marconi silver proof) £60

* Coins marked thus were originally issued in Royal Mint sets.

| K12 | K13 | K14 | K15 |

K12 **Two pounds.** Commonwealth Games commemorative. England. R̵. A moving figure of an athlete holding a banner, the top of which being divided into lines to symbolise lanes of a running track or swimming pool with a cameo of the English flag and the inscription 'XVII COMMONWEALTH GAMES 2002' and the denomination '£2'. Edge inscription 'SPIRIT OF FRIENDSHIP. MANCHESTER 2002'. (Reverse design: Matthew Bonaccorsi)

2002..£7
— Specimen (in Presentation set, see US24)*...£10
— Proof *FDC* (in set, see PS76)*...£12
— Proof in Silver *FDC* (in set, see PSS12)* £35
— Proof in gold *FDC* (in set, see PCGS1)* £750

K12A As above but with colour added to the flag and parts of the banner, Proof Piedfort in Silver *FDC* (in set, see PSS13)*..£80

K13 **Two pounds.** Commonwealth Games commemorative. R̵. Northern Ireland. As above but with a cameo of the Northern Ireland flag. Edge inscription 'SPIRIT OF FRIENDSHIP. MANCHESTER 2002'. (Reverse design: Matthew Bonaccorsi)

2002..£7
— Specimen (in Presentation set, see US24)*...£10
— Proof *FDC* (in set, see PS76)*...£12
— Proof in Silver *FDC* (in set, see PSS12)* £35
— Proof in gold *FDC* (in set, see PCGS1)* £750

K13A As above but with colour added to the flag and parts of the banner, Proof Piedfort in Silver *FDC* (in set, see PSS13)*..£80

K14 **Two pounds.** Commonwealth Games commemorative. R̵. Scotland. As above but with a cameo of the Scottish flag. Edge inscription 'SPIRIT OF FRIENDSHIP. MANCHESTER 2002'.(Reverse design: Matthew Bonaccorsi)

2002..£7
— Specimen (in Presentation set, see US24)*...£10
— Proof *FDC* (in set, see PS76)*...£12
— Proof in Silver *FDC* (in set, see PSS12)* £35
— Proof in gold *FDC* (in set, see PCGS1)* £750

K14A As above but with colour added to the flag and parts of the banner, Proof Piedfort in Silver *FDC* (in set, see PSS13)*..£80

K15 **Two pounds.** Commonwealth Games commemorative. R̵. Wales. As above but with a cameo of the Welsh flag. Edge inscription 'SPIRIT OF FRIENDSHIP. MANCHESTER 2002'. (Reverse design: Matthew Bonaccorsi)

2002..£7
— Specimen (in Presentation set, see US24)*...£10
— Proof *FDC* (in set, see PS76)*...£12
— Proof in Silver *FDC* (in set, see PSS12)* £35
— Proof in gold *FDC* (in set, see PCGS1)* £750

K15A As above but with colour added to the flag and parts of the banner, Proof Piedfort in Silver *FDC* (in set, see PSS13)*..£80

* Coins marked thus were originally issued in Royal Mint sets.

K16   K17   K18   K19

K16 **Two pounds.** Discovery of the structure of DNA. England. ℞. In the centre the spiralling
double helix structure of DNA with the inscription 'DNA DOUBLE HELIX' and the
dates '1953' and '2003' separated by the denomination 'TWO POUNDS' Edge:
'DEOXYRIBONUCLEIC ACID'. (Reverse design: John Mills)
2003..£5
—   Specimen in presentation folder (Issued: 41,568)..£10
—   Proof *FDC* (in set, see PS78)*...£10
—   Proof in Silver *FDC* (Issued: 11,204) £35
—   Proof piedfort in silver *FDC* (Issued: 8,728) £60
—   Proof in gold *FDC* (Issued: 1,500)..£750

K17 **Two pounds.** ℞.In the centre a depiction of Trevithick's Locomotive Penydarren and
the denomination 'TWO POUNDS' surrounded by a cog representing the Industrial
Revolution and the inscription 'R.TREVITHICK 1804 INVENTION INDUSTRY
PROGRESS 2004' Patterned Edge. (Reverse design: Robert Lowe)
2004..£5
—   Specimen in presentation folder (Issued: 56,871)..£10
—   Brilliant uncirculated in silver (Issued: 1,923)..£25
—   Proof *FDC* (in 2004 set, see PS81)*...£10
—   Proof in Silver *FDC* (Issued: 10,233) £35
—   Proof piedfort in silver *FDC* (Issued: 5,303) ....£ 65
—   Proof in gold *FDC* (1,500)..£750

K18 **Two pounds.** 400th Anniversary of the Gunpowder Plot. ℞. An arrangement of crosiers,
maces and swords, surrounded by stars, with the dates '1605' and '2005' above, and the
denomination 'TWO POUNDS' below, and the edge inscription REMEMBER
REMEMBER THE FIFTH OF NOVEMBER'. (Reverse design: Peter Forster)
2005..£5
—   Specimen in presentation folder (Issued: 12,044)..£7
—   Proof *FDC* (in 2005 set, see PS84)*...£10
—   Proof in Silver *FDC* (Issued: 4,394) £40
—   Proof piedfort in silver *FDC* (Issued: 4,585) £65
—   Proof in gold *FDC* (Issued: 914)..£750

K19 **Two pounds.** 60th Anniversary of the end of World War II. ℞. In the centre a depiction of
the front of St.Paul's Cathedral in full floodlights with the denomination 'TWO POUNDS'
and the dates '1945 - 2005' with the edge inscription 'IN VICTORY MAGNANIMITY IN
PEACE GOODWILL'. (Reverse design: Robert Elderton)
2005..£5
—   Specimen in presentation folder with medal (Issued: 53,686)................................£10
—   Proof in Silver *FDC* (Issued: 21,734) £35
—   Proof piedfort in silver *FDC* (Issued: 4,798) £65
—   Proof in gold *FDC* (Issued: 1,578 single coins and 1,346 in sets)........................ £750

* Coins marked thus were originally issued in Royal Mint sets.

| K20 | K21 | K22 |

K20 **Two pounds.** 200th Anniversary of the birth of Isambard Brunel. ℞. In the centre a portrait of the engineer with segments of a wheel and bridge in the background surrounded by links of a heavy chain and the date '2006' and the denomination 'TWO POUNDS', with the edge inscription '1806 - 1859 ISAMBARD KINGDOM BRUNEL ENGINEER'. (Reverse design: Rod Kelly)

2006..£5
— Specimen in presentation folder (with K21)...£10
— Proof *FDC* (in 2006 set, see PS87)*...£10
— Proof in silver *FDC* (Issued: 7,251)..£35
— Proof piedfort in silver *FDC* (Issued: 3,199) (see PSS25)* £65
— Proof in gold *FDC* (Issued: 1,071)..£750

K21 **Two pounds.** 200th Anniversary of the birth of Isambard Brunel. ℞. In the centre a section of the roof of Paddington Station with 'BRUNEL' below and the date '2006' and the denomination 'TWO POUNDS', with the edge inscription 'SO MANY IRONS IN THE FIRE'. (Reverse design: Robert Evans)

2006..£4
— Specimen in presentation folder (with K20)...£10
— Proof *FDC* (in 2006 set, see PS87)*...£10
— Proof in silver *FDC* (Issued: 5,375)..£35
— Proof piedfort in silver *FDC* (Issued: 3,018) (see PSS25)*.....................£65
— Proof in gold *FDC* (Issued: 746)...£750

K22 **Two pounds.** Tercentenary of the Act of Union between England and Scotland. ℞. A design dividing the coin into four quarters, with a rose and a thistle occupying two of the quarters, and a portcullis in each of the other two quarters. The whole is overlaid with a linking jigsaw motif and surrounded by the dates '1707' and '2007' and the denomination 'TWO POUNDS', with an edge inscription 'UNITED INTO ONE KINGDOM' (Reverse design : Yvonne Holton)

2007..£5
— Specimen in presentation folder..£8
— Proof *FDC* (in 2007 set, see PS90)*...£10
— Proof in Silver *FDC* (Issued: 8,310) £35
— Proof piedfort in silver *FDC* (Issued: 4,000) £60
— Proof in gold *FDC* (Issued: 750)...£700

K22A **— Error edge.** The obverse and reverse designs of the Act of Union silver proof combined with the edge inscription of the Abolition of Slave Trade issue (K23 below). The edge inscription is impressed on the blanks prior to the striking of the obverse and reverse designs and whilst one example has been reported, and confirmed as genuine by the Royal Mint, it seems possible that a small batch may have been produced and other pieces have yet to be detected. £1000

* Coins marked thus were originally issued in Royal Mint sets.

| K23 | K24 | K25 |

K23 **Two pounds.** Bicentenary of the Abolition of the Slave Trade in the British Empire.
R. The date '1807' with the '0' depicted as a broken chain link , surrounded by the
inscription 'AN ACT FOR THE ABOLITION OF THE SLAVE TRADE', and the
date '2007', with an edge inscription 'AM I NOT A MAN, AND A BROTHER'
(Reverse design : David Gentleman)

2007..£5
— Specimen in presentation folder with..£8
— Proof *FDC* (in 2007 set, see PS90)* £10
— Proof in Silver *FDC* (Issued: 7,095) £35
— Proof piedfort in silver *FDC* (Issued: 3,990)* £60
— Proof in gold *FDC* (Issued: 1,000)..£750

K24 **Two pounds.** 250th Anniversary of the birth of Robert Burns. R. A design featuring
a quote from the song *Auld Lang Syne* 'WE'LL TAK A CUP A' KINDNESS YET,
FOR AULD LANG SYNE ', the calligraphy of which is based on the handwriting of
Robert Burns with the inscription '1759 ROBERT BURNS 1796' and the denomination
'TWO POUNDS' with the edge inscription 'SHOULD AULD ACQUAINTANCE BE
FORGOT' (Reverse design: Royal Mint Engraving Team)

2009..£5
— Specimen in celebration card (Issued: 120,223) £6
— Specimen in presentation folder (Edition: 50,000) £8
— Proof *FDC* (in 2009 set, see PS97)* £10
— Proof in Silver *FDC* (Issued: 9,188))...£35
— Proof piedfort in silver *FDC* (Issued: 3,500) £60
— Proof in gold *FDC* (Issued: 1,000)..£750

K25 **Two pounds.** 200th Anniversary of the birth of Charles Darwin. R A design showing a
portrait of Charles Darwin facing an ape surrounded by the inscription '1809 DARWIN
2009' and the denomination 'TWO POUNDS' and the edge inscription 'ON THE
ORIGIN OF SPECIES 1859' (Reverse design: Suzie Zamit)

2009..£5
— Specimen in presentation folder (Edition: 25,000) £8
— Proof *FDC* (in 2009 set, see PS97)* £10
— Proof in Silver *FDC* (Issued: 9,357))...£35
— Proof piedfort in silver *FDC* (Issued: 3,282) £60
— Proof in gold *FDC* (Issued: 1,000)..£750

* Coins marked thus were originally issued in Royal Mint sets.

K26

K26 **Two pounds.** The Centenary of the death of Florence Nightingale and the One hundred and fiftieth Anniversary of the publication of *NOTES ON NURSING*. ℞. A design depicting the pulse of a patient being taken, surrounded by the inscription 'FLORENCE NIGHTINGALE – 1910' and the denomination 'TWO POUNDS'. The design being set against a background texture of lines symbolising rays of light from a lamp with the edge inscription '150 YEARS OF NURSING' on the precious metal versions. (Reverse design: Gordon Summers)

2010...£3
— Specimen on presentation card £5
— Specimen in presentation folder (Edition: 25,000)....................................£8
— Proof *FDC* (in 2010 set, see PS101)*..£10
— Proof in silver *FDC* (Issued: 5,117)...£35
— Proof piedfort in silver *FDC* (Issued: 2770) £60
— Proof in gold *FDC* (Issued: 472)...£750

K27

K27 **Two pounds.** 500th Anniversary of the launch of the Mary Rose. R. A depiction of the ship based on a contemporary painting, surrounded by a cartouche bearing the inscription 'THE MARY ROSE' above, the denomination 'TWO POUNDS' below, and a rose to the left and right. The lettering on the reverse is rendered in the Lombardic style employed on the coins of Henry VII, and with the edge inscription 'YOUR NOBLEST SHIPPE 1511' (Reverse design: John Bergdahl)

2011...£3
— Specimen in presentation folder (Edition: 20,000).....................................£8
— Proof *FDC* (in 2011 set, see PS104)*..£10
— Proof in silver *FDC* (Issued: 6,618)...£50
— Proof piedfort in silver *FDC* (Issued: 2,394)...£88
— Proof in gold *FDC* (Issued: 692) £800

* Coins marked thus were originally issued in Royal Mint sets.

K28   K29   K30

K28 **Two pounds.** The 400th Anniversary of the King James Bible. R. A design
focusing on the opening verse of St John's Gospel, 'IN THE BEGINNING WAS
THE WORD', showing the verse as printing blocks on the left and the printed
page on the right, with the inscription' KING JAMES BIBLE' above and the dates
'1611-2011'below with the edge inscription 'THE AUTHORISED VERSION'.
(Reverse design: Paul Stafford and Benjamin Wright)

2011...£3
— Specimen in presentation folder (Edition: 20,000)..£8
— Proof *FDC* (in 2011 set, see PS104)*...£10
— Proof in silver *FDC* (Issued: 4,494)..£50
— Proof piedfort in silver *FDC* (Issued: 2,394)..£88
— Proof in gold *FDC* (Issued: 355) £800

K29 **Two pounds.** The 200th Anniversary of the birth of Charles Dickens. R. A
silhouette profile of the writer through the titles of his works, greater prominence
being given to those that are more well known, with the inscription 'CHARLES
DICKENS 1870' to the left with the edge inscription 'SOMETHING WILL TURN
UP' (Reverse design:)

2012...£3
— Specimen in presentation folder (Issued: 15,035)..£8
— Proof *FDC* (in 2012 set, see PS107)* £10
— Proof in silver *FDC* (Issued: 2,631) £50
— Proof piedfort in silver *FDC* (Issued: 1,279) £88
— Proof in gold *FDC* (Issued: 202)..£800

K30 **Two pounds.** 350th Anniversary of the Guinea, R. A depiction of the Royal Arms
based on that on the reverse of the 'SPADE GUINEA' of George III with and
surrounded by the inscription 'ANNIVERSARY OF THE GOLDEN GUINEA'
and the date '2013' below with the edge inscription 'WHAT IS A GUINEA ? 'TIS
A SPENDID THING'. (Reverse design: Anthony Smith).

2013...£4
— Specimen in presentation folder..£10
— Proof *FDC* (in 2013 set, see PS109)* £10
— Proof in silver *FDC* (Issued: 1,640) £50
— Proof piedfort in silver *FDC* (Issued: 969) £100
— Proof in gold *FDC* (Issued: 284)..£900

* Coins marked thus were originally issued in Royal Mint sets.

K31   K32

K31   **Two pounds.** 150th Anniversary of the London Underground. R.The Roundel logo of the London underground system with the dates '1863' above and '2013' below and the edge inscription 'MIND THE GAP'. (Reverse design: Edwina Ellis).

2013 .... £4
—   Specimen in presentation folder with K32 .... £20
—   Proof *FDC* (in 2013 set, see PS109)* £10
—   Proof in silver *FDC* (Issued: 1,185) £50
—   Proof piedfort in silver *FDC* (Issued: 162) £100
—   Proof in gold *FDC* (Issued: 132) £900

K32   **Two pounds.** 150th Anniversary of the London Underground. R. Depicts a train emerging from a tunnel with the date '1863' to the left and the inscription 'LONDON UNDERGROUND' and the date '2013' to the right with a patterned edge inspired by the map of the underground network. (Reverse design: Edward Barber and Jay Osgerby).

2013 .... £4
—   Specimen in presentation folder with K31 .... £20
—   Proof *FDC* (in 2013 set, see PS109)* £10
—   Proof in silver *FDC* (Edition: Issued: 2,042) £50
—   Proof piedfort in silver *FDC* (Issued: 186) £100
—   Proof in gold *FDC* (Issued: 140) £900

K33

K33   **Two pounds.** Trinity House R. A depiction of a lighthouse lens, surrounded by the inscription 'TRINITY HOUSE' and the dates '1514' and '2014' with the denomination 'TWO POUNDS' with the edge inscription 'SERVING THE MARINER' (Reverse design: Joe Whitlock Blundell with David Eccles).

2014 .... £4
—   Specimen in presentation folder £10
—   Proof *FDC* (in 2014 set, see PS112)* £10
—   Proof in silver *FDC* (Edition: 3,714 including coins in sets) £50
—   Proof piedfort in silver *FDC* (Edition: 3,514 including coins in sets) £100
—   Proof in gold *FDC* (Edition: including coins in sets) £900

* Coins marked thus were originally issued in Royal Mint sets.

K34

K34 Two pounds. World War I R. A depiction pf Lord Kitchener pointing, with the inscription 'YOUR COUNTRY NEEDS YOU' below the effigy of Lord Kitchener, and the inscription 'THE FIRST WORLD WAR 1914-1918' and the date '2014' with the edge inscription 'THE LAMPS ARE GOING OUT ALL OVER EUROPE' (Reverse design: John Bergdahl).

2014..£4
— Specimen in presentation folder...£10
— Proof *FDC* (in 2014 set, see PS112)*...£10
— Proof in silver *FDC* (Edition: 8,014 including coins in sets) £50
— Proof piedfort in silver *FDC* (Edition: 4,514 including coins in sets)..................£100
— Proof in gold *FDC* (Edition: 825 including coins in sets)....................................£750

K35

K35 Two pounds. World War 1 – The Royal Navy R. The designs shows a dreadnought at sea with the inscription 'THE FIRST WORLD WAR 1914 – 1918' and the date of the year below with the edged inscription 'THE SURE SHIELD OF BRITAIN' (Reverse design : David Rowlands).

2015
— BU in presentation pack £10
— Proof *FDC* (in 2015 set, see PS117) * £5
— Proof in silver *FDC* (Edition: 8,500 including coins in sets)...............................£50
— Proof piedfort in silver *FDC* (Edition: 4,000 including coins in sets)..................£100
— Proof in gold *FDC* (Edition: 900) £750

* Coins marked thus were originally issued in Royal Mint sets.

K36

K36 Two pounds. 800th Anniversary of the signing of Magna Carta R. The design shows King John flanked by figures representing the clergy on one side and the barons on the other with the inscription 'MAGNA CARTA' and '1215 – 2015' and the edge inscription ' FOUNDATION OF LIBERTY'. (Reverse design: John Bergdahl).

2015
— BU in presentation pack £10
— Proof *FDC* (in 2015 set, see PS117) * £5
— Proof in silver *FDC* (Edition: 3,000 see PSS64)*
— Proof piedfort in silver *FDC* (Edition: 1,500)..£100
— Proof in gold *FDC* (Edition: 100)..£1000

Obverse portrait by Jody Clark

K36A

K36A Two pounds. 800th Anniversary of the signing of Magna Carta. R. As above.
2015
— Proof in silver *FDC* (Edition: 7,500)
— Proof piedfort in silver *FDC* (Edition: 2,000)..£100
— Proof in gold *FDC* (Edition: 500)..£1000

* Coins marked thus were originally issued in Royal Mint sets.

K37

K37 Two pounds. R. A depiction of Britannia holding a shield and trident with the
inscription 'TWO POUNDS' and the edge inscription 'QUATUOR MARIA
VINDICO' (Reverse design: Antony Dufort).
2015
— Proof *FDC* (in 2015 set, see PS116)* £5
— Proof in silver *FDC* (Edition: 7,500 see PSS63)* £50
— Proof in gold *FDC* (Edition: 500 see PGC4P) * £750
— Proof piedfort in platinum *FDC* (Edition:)
2016
— Proof *FDC* (in 2016 set, see PS119)*...£5
— Proof in silver *FDC* (Edition: 7,500 see PSS68)*

For further £2 commemorative issues, see Olympic and Paralympic coins on page 143.
* *Coins marked thus were originally issued in Royal Mint sets.*

K38

K38 **Two pounds.** Honouring the work of William Shakespeare. Comedy. R. A cap and bells with a Jester's stick accompanied by the inscription 'WILLIAM SHAKESPEARE 2016' with the edge inscription 'ALL THE WORLD'S A STAGE'.(Reverse design John Bergdahl).

2016
— Specimen in presentation folder of three £2 coins - Comedy, History & Tragedy.........£28
— Proof *FDC* (in 2016 set, see PS119)* £15
— Proof in silver *FDC* (Edition: 5,000) £60
— Proof piedfort in silver *FDC* (Edition : 2,500)...£100
— Proof in gold *FDC* (Edition : 300)...£695

K39   K40

K39 **Two pounds.** Honouring the work of William Shakespeare. History. R. A dagger through a crown accompanied by the inscription 'WILLIAM SHAKESPEARE 2016' with the edge inscription 'THE HOLLOW CROWN'. (Reverse design: John Bergdahl).

2016
— Specimen in presentation folder of three £2 coins - Comedy, History & Tragedy.........£28
— Proof *FDC* (in 2016 set, see PS119)* £15
— Proof in silver *FDC* (Edition: 5,000) £60
— Proof piedfort in silver *FDC* (Edition : 2,500)...£100
— Proof in gold *FDC* (Edition : 300)...£695

K40 **Two pounds.** Honouring the work of William Shakespeare. Tragedy. R. A skull next to a rose accompanied by the inscription 'WILLIAM SHAKESPEARE 2016' with the edge inscription 'WHAT A PIECE OF WORK IS A MAN'. (Reverse design John Bergdahl).

2016
— Specimen in presentation folder of three £2 coins - Comedy, History & Tragedy.........£28
— Proof *FDC* (in 2016 set, see PS119)* £15
— Proof in silver *FDC* (Edition: 5,000) £60
— Proof piedfort in silver *FDC* (Edition : 2,500)...£100
— Proof in gold *FDC* (Edition : 300)...£695

K41

K41 **Two pounds.** World War 1.The Army. R. A stylised silhouette of the heads of three
soldiers and references the English cubism movement prevalent around the time of
the First World War with the inscription 'THE FIRST WORLD WAR 1914 – 1918',
and the date of the year with the edge inscription 'FOR KING AND COUNTRY'.
(Reverse design: John Bergdahl).
2016
— Specimen in presentation folder...£10
— Proof *FDC* (in 2016 set, see PS119)* £15
— Proof in silver *FDC* (Edition: 8,500 including coins in sets).......................................£60
— Proof piedfort in silver *FDC* (Edition : 5,000 including coins in sets).......................£100
— Proof in gold *FDC* (Edition: 950 including coins in sets)...£695

K42

K42 **Two pounds.** Three hundred and fifty Anniversary of the Great Fire of London. R.
A view across the River Thames of the City of London in flames with boats fleeing
the burning city with the inscription '1666 THE GREAT FIRE OF LONDON
2016' with the edge inscription 'THE WHOLE CITY IN DREADFUL FLAMES'.
(Reverse design: Aaron West)
2016
— Specimen in presentation folder...£10
— Proof *FDC* (in 2016 set, see PS119)*...£15
— Proof in silver *FDC* (Edition: 10,500)..£60
— Proof piedfort in silver *FDC* (Edition : 5,000)..£100
— Proof in gold *FDC* (Edition : 950)..£750

CUPRO-NICKEL

Note for Collectors

The collecting of crown size coins is one of the most popular pursuits among new and established coin collectors. Before decimalisation in 1971, crowns had a nominal denomination of five shillings and this was then changed to twenty five pence in 1972 when the Silver Wedding commemorative was issued. Over time with increasing metal, manufacturing and distribution costs, the production of coins with such a low face value was not economic and the decision was taken to change to a higher value that would last for many years. The first of the five pound crowns was issued in 1990 to mark the ninetieth birthday of The Queen Mother. It seems sensible to group all of the crown size coins together and therefore the earlier twenty five pence issues are not listed between the twenty pence and fifty pence denominations but appear below.

Obverse portrait by Arnold Machin

LL1

LL1 Twenty-five pence (crown). Silver Wedding Commemorative R. The initials E P on a background of foliage, figure of Eros above the Royal Crown with the inscription 'ELIZABETH AND PHILIP' above and the dates '20 NOVEMBER 1947 – 1972' below.(Reverse design: Arnold Machin)

1972..£2
— Proof *FDC* (in 1972 Set, See PS22)*...£6
— Silver proof *FDC* (Issued: 100,000) £45

LL2

LL2 Twenty-five pence (crown). Silver Jubilee Commemorative R. The Ampulla and Anointing Spoon encircled by a floral border and above a Royal Crown. (Obverse and reverse design: Arnold Machin)

1977..£2
— Specimen in presentation folder...£2
— Proof *FDC* (in 1977 Set, See PS27)*...£5
— Silver proof *FDC* (Issued: 377,000) £40

* *Coins marked thus were originally issued in Royal Mint sets.*

LL3   LL4

LL3 **Twenty-Five pence** (crown). Queen Mother 80th Birthday Commemorative R. In the centre a portrait of The Queen Mother surrounded by bows and lions with the inscription 'QUEEN ELIZABETH THE QUEEN MOTHER 4 AUGUST 1980' (Reverse design: Richard Guyatt)

1980..£3
— Specimen in presentation folder...£5
— Silver proof *FDC* (Issued: 83,672) £45

LL4 **Twenty-five pence.**(crown). Royal Wedding Commemorative R.Portrait of the Prince of Wales and Lady Diana Spencer with the inscription 'HRH THE PRINCE OF WALES AND LADY DIANA SPENCER 1981' (Reverse design: Philip Nathan)

1981..£3
— Specimen in presentation folder...£5
— Silver proof *FDC* (Issued: 218,142) £45

Obverse portrait by Raphael Maklouf

L1

L1 **Five pounds** (crown). Queen Mother's 90th birthday commemorative. R. A Cypher in the letter E in duplicate above a Royal Crown flanked by a rose and a thistle all within the inscription 'QUEEN ELIZABETH THE QUEEN MOTHER' and the dates '1900 – 1990' (Reverse design: Leslie Durbin)

1990...£10
— Specimen in presentation folder (Issued: 45,250)..£12
— Proof in silver *FDC* (Issued: 56,102)...£45
— Proof in gold *FDC* (Issued: 2,500)..£1800

* Coins marked thus were originally issued in Royal Mint sets.

L2

L2 **Five pounds** (crown). 40th Anniversary of the Coronation. ℞. St Edward's Crown encircled by forty trumpets all within the inscription 'FAITH AND TRUTH I WILL BEAR UNTO YOU' and the dates '1953 – 1993'(Reverse design: Robert Elderton)

1993..£7
— Specimen in presentation folder...£9
— Proof *FDC* (in 1993 set, see PS51)*..£12
— Proof in silver *FDC* (Issued: 58,877)..£45
— Proof in gold *FDC* (Issued: 2,500)..£1800

L3

L3 **Five pounds** (crown). 70th Birthday of Queen Elizabeth II. ℞. A representation of Windsor Castle with five flag poles, two holding forked pennants with anniversary dates '1926' and '1996', the other flags are Royal Arms, the Union flag and Our Personal flag. Edge inscription: 'VIVAT REGINA ELIZABETHA'. (Reverse design: Avril Vaughan)

1996...£10
— Specimen in presentation folder (issued: 73,311)...£12
— Proof *FDC* (in 1996 set, See PS57)*..£12
— Proof in silver *FDC* (Issued: 39,336)..£50
— Proof in gold *FDC* (Issued: 2,127)..£1800

* Coins marked thus were originally issued in Royal Mint sets.

L4

L4   **Five pounds** (crown). Golden Wedding of Queen Elizabeth II and Prince Philip.
Conjoint portraits of The Queen and Prince Philip. ℞. A pair of shields, chevronwise, on
the left, OurRoyal Arms, on the right, the shield of Prince Philip, above a Royal Crown
separating the dates '1947' and '1997' with the date '20 NOVEMBER', below an
anchor cabled with the denomination 'FIVE POUNDS'.
(Obverse design: Philip Nathan, reverse design: Leslie Durbin)
1997..£7
  —   Specimen in presentation folder...£10
  —   Proof *FDC* (in 1997 set, See PS59)* £15
  —   Proof in silver *FDC* (Issued: 33,689)...£50
  —   Proof in gold *FDC* (Issued: 2,574)...£1800

Obverse portrait by Ian Rank-Broadley

L5

L5   **Five pounds** (crown). Prince Charles' 50th Birthday. ℞. A portrait of Prince
Charles **a**nd in the background words relating to the work of The Prince's Trust.
A circumscription of 'FIFIETH BIRTHDAY OF HRH PRINCE OF WALES' and
below 'FIVE POUNDS' flanked by the anniversary dates '1948' and '1998'.
(Reverse design: Michael Noakes / Robert Elderton)
1998..£7
  —   Specimen in presentation folder...£10
  —   Proof *FDC* (in 1998 set, see PS61)* £15
  —   Proof in silver *FDC* (Issued: 13,379)...£60
  —   Proof in gold *FDC* (Issued: 773)...£1800

* Coins marked thus were originally issued in Royal Mint sets.

L6

L6 **Five pounds** (crown). Diana, Princess of Wales Memorial. R. A portrait of Diana, Princess of Wales with the dates '1961' and '1997', and the circumscription 'IN MEMORY OF DIANA, PRINCESS OF WALES' with the value 'FIVE POUNDS' (Reverse design: David Cornell)

1999...	£7
— Specimen in presentation folder..	£12
— Proof *FDC* (in 1999 set, see PS63)*...	£15
— Proof in silver *FDC* (Issued: 49,545)...	£50
— Proof in gold *FDC* (Issued: 7,500)...	£2500

L7   L7A

L7 **Five pounds** (crown). Millennium commemorative. R. A representation of the dial of a clock with hands set at 12 o'clock with a map of the British Isles and the dates '1999' and '2000' and the words 'ANNO DOMINI' and the value 'FIVE POUNDS'. Edge: 'WHAT'S PAST IS PROLOGUE' in serif or sans serif font. (Reverse design: Jeffrey Matthews)

1999...	£7
— Specimen in presentation folder..	£10
— Proof in silver *FDC* (Issued: 49,057)...	£50
— Proof in gold *FDC* (Issued: 2,500)...	£1650
2000	
— Specimen in presentation folder..	£20
— Proof *FDC* (in 2000 set, see PS65)*...	£15
— Proof in gold *FDC* (Issued: 1,487)...	£1650

L7A 2000

— Specimen in presentation folder with Dome mint mark	£20

      (See illustration above - the mintmark is located within the shaded area at 3 o'clock).

L7B 2000

— Proof in silver *FDC* (Issued: 14,255)..	£60

(The reverse design is the same as the 1999 issue but with the British Isles highlighted with 22 ct. gold)

* Coins marked thus were originally issued in Royal Mint sets.

| L8 | L9 |

L8   **Five pounds** (crown). Queen Mother commemorative. R. A portrait of the Queen
Mother flanked by groups of people with the circumscription 'QUEEN ELIZABETH
THE QUEEN MOTHER' the anniversary dates '1900' and '2000' below, and the
denomination 'FIVE POUNDS'. Below the portrait a representation of her signature.
(Reverse design: Ian Rank-Broadley)

2000..£7
—   Specimen in presentation folder...£10
—   Proof in silver *FDC* (Issued: 31,316)...£50
—   Proof piedfort in silver *FDC* (Issued: 14,850) £80
—   Proof in gold *FDC* (Issued: 3,000)..£1650

L9   **Five pounds** (crown). Victorian anniversary. R. A classic portrait of the young Queen
Victoria based on the Penny Black postage stamp with a V representing Victoria, and
taking the form of railway lines and in the background the iron framework of the Crystal
Palace, and the denomination '5 POUNDS' and the dates '1901' and '2001'.
(Reverse design: Mary Milner-Dickens)

2001..£7
—   Specimen in presentation folder...£10
—   Proof *FDC* (in 2001 set, see PS68)*..£15
—   Proof in silver *FDC* (Issued: 19,216)..£55
—   Proof in gold *FDC* (Issued: 2,098)..£1650

L9A —   Proof in silver *FDC* with 'reverse frosting' giving matt appearance (Issued:596)
(Crown issued with sovereigns of 1901 and 2001)*...£200
L9B —   Proof in gold *FDC* with 'reverse frosting' giving matt appearance.(Issued:733)
(Crown issued with four different type sovereigns of Queen Victoria, - Young
Head with shield, and Young Head with St.George reverse, Jubilee Head and
Old Head.)* £1850

* Coins marked thus were originally issued in Royal Mint sets.

L10

L10 **Five pounds** (crown). Golden Jubilee commemorative 2002. O. New portrait of The Queen with the denomination 'FIVE POUNDS'. ℞. Equestrian portrait of The Queen with the inscription 'ELIZABETH II DEI GRA REGINA FID DEF' around the circumference and 'AMOR POPULI PRAESIDIUM REG' within, and the date '2002' below separated by the central element of the Royal Arms.
(Obverse and reverse designs: Ian Rank-Broadley)

2002..£7
— Specimen in presentation folder...£10
— Proof *FDC* (in 2002 set, see PS72)*...£15
— Proof in silver *FDC* (Issued: 54,012)..£55
— Proof in gold *FDC* (Issued: 3,500)..£1650

L11

L11 **Five pounds** (crown). Queen Mother Memorial 2002. ℞. Three quarter portrait of the Queen Mother within a wreath with the inscription 'QUEEN ELIZABETH THE QUEEN MOTHER' and the dates '1900' and '2002', with an edge inscription 'STRENGTH, DIGNITY AND LAUGHTER'. (Reverse design: Avril Vaughan)

2002..£8
— Specimen in presentation folder...£15
— Proof in silver *FDC* (Issued: 16,117)..£55
— Proof in gold *FDC* (Issued: 2,086)..£1650

* Coins marked thus were originally issued in Royal Mint sets.

L12

L12   **Five pounds** (crown). Coronation commemorative 2003. O. Profile portrait of
The Queen in linear form facing right with the inscription 'ELIZABETH II DEI
GRATIA REGINA F D'. R. In the centre the inscription 'GOD SAVE THE QUEEN'
surrounded by the inscription 'CORONATION JUBILEE' the denomination 'FIVE
POUNDS' and the date '2003'. (Obverse and reverse designs: Tom Phillips)
2003..£8
—   Specimen in presentation folder (Issued: 100,481)...£10
—   Proof *FDC* (in 2003 set, see PS78)*...£15
—   Proof in silver *FDC* (Issued: 28,758)..£55
—   Proof in gold *FDC* (Issued: 1,896)..£1800

L13

L13   **Five pounds** (crown). Centenary of Entente Cordiale 2004. R. In the centre the head
and shoulders of Britannia and her French counterpart Marianne with the inscription
'ENTENTE CORDIALE' separated by the dates '1904' and '2004'. Obv. as 4556.
(Reverse design: David Gentleman)
2004..£8
—   Specimen in presentation folder (Issued: 16,507)...£20
—   Proof *FDC* with reverse frosting (Issued: 6,065)...£20
—   Proof in silver *FDC* (Issued: 11,295)..£60
—   Proof Piedfort in silver *FDC* (Issued: 2,500)...£150
—   Proof in gold *FDC* (Issued: 926)..£1800
—   Proof Piedfort in platinum *FDC* (Issued: 501)..£4000

* Coins marked thus were originally issued in Royal Mint sets.

L14   L15

L14 **Five pounds** (crown). Two hundredth anniversary of the Battle of Trafalgar 2005. ℞. A depiction of the two British ships, HMS Victory and Temeraine, in the midst of the battle, the central design surrounded by the inscription 'TRAFALGAR' and the dates '1805' and '2005' with the edge inscription 'ENGLAND EXPECTS THAT EVERY MAN WILL DO HIS DUTY'. Obv. as 4556. (Reverse design: Clive Duncan)
Note: Only the precious metal versions have edge inscriptions, the CuNi coins have a milled edge.
2005..£9
  —   Specimen in presentation folder (Issued: 79,868)..£12
  —   Proof *FDC* (in 2005 set, see PS84)* £12
  —   Proof in silver *FDC* (Issued: 21,448)..£55
  —   Proof piedfort in silver *FDC* (see PSS21)*...£90
  —   Proof in gold *FDC* (Issued: 1,805)...£1750

L15 **Five pounds** (crown). Two hundredth anniversary of the death of Nelson 2005. ℞. A portrait of Lord Nelson in the uniform of a Vice Admiral accompanied by the inscription 'HORATIO NELSON' and the dates '1805' and '2005' with the edge inscription 'ENGLAND EXPECTS THAT EVERY MAN WILL DO HIS DUTY'. Obv. as 4556. (Reverse design: James Butler)
Note: Only the precious metal versions have edge inscriptions, the CuNi coins have a milled edge.
2005..£10
  —   Specimen in presentation folder (Issued: 72,498)..£12
  —   Proof *FDC* (in 2005 set, see PS84)* £12
  —   Proof in silver *FDC* (Issued: 12,852)..£60
  —   Proof piedfort in silver *FDC* (see PSS21)*...£90
  —   Proof in gold *FDC* (Issued: 1,760) £1750
  —   Proof piedfort in platinum *FDC* (Edition: 200) £4000

* Coins marked thus were originally issued in Royal Mint sets.

L16

L16 **Five pounds** (crown). 80th Birthday of Her Majesty Queen Elizabeth II. ℞. A fanfare of
regal trumpets with the inscription 'VIVAT REGINA' and the dates '1926' and '2006',
and the edge inscription 'DUTY SERVICE FAITH'. Obv. as 4556.
(Reverse design: Danuta Solowiej-Wedderburn)
2006...£7
— Specimen in presentation folder...£10
— Proof *FDC* (in 2006 set, see PS87)*...£15
— Proof in silver *FDC* (Issued: 20,790)...£55
— Proof in gold *FDC* (Issued: 2,750)...£1800
— Proof piedfort in platinum *FDC* (Issued: 250)..£4000
L16A — Proof piedfort in silver with selected gold plating *FDC* (Issued: 5,000).................£80

L17

L17 **Five pounds** (crown). Diamond Wedding Anniversary of Her Majesty Queen
Elizabeth II and The Duke of Edinburgh. O. Conjoint portrait of The Queen and
Prince Philip. ℞. The Rose window of Westminster Abbey with the inscription
'TVEATVR VNITA DEVS', the dates '1947' and '2007', the denomination 'FIVE
POUNDS', and the edge inscription 'MY STRENGTH AND STAY'
(Obverse design: Ian Rank-Broadley, reverse design: Emma Noble)
2007...£7
— Specimen in presentation folder...£10
— Proof *FDC* (in 2007 set, see PS90)*...£15
— Proof in silver *FDC* (Issued: 15,186)...£55
— Proof piedfort in silver *FDC* (Issued: 2,000)...£80
— Proof in gold *FDC* (Issued: 2,380)...£1800
— Proof piedfort in platinum *FDC* (Issued: 250)..£4000

* Coins marked thus were originally issued in Royal Mint sets.

L18   L19

L18 **Five pounds** (crown). 450th Anniversary of the Accession of Queen Elizabeth I. R A portrait of Queen Elizabeth I surrounded by four Tudor roses placed at the centre points of connecting arches, with two side panels containing details taken from carvings made by Robert Dudley, Earlof Leicester, found at the Tower of London, the design being encircled by the inscription 'ELIZABETH REGINA' with the dates 'MDLVIII' and 'MMVIII' with the edge inscription 'I HAVE REIGNED WITH YOUR LOVES' on the precious metal versions. Obv. as 4556. (Reverse design: Rod Kelly).

2008...£7
— Specimen in presentation folder (Issued: 26,700)..................................£10
— Proof *FDC* (in 2008 set, see PS93)*...£15
— Proof in silver *FDC* (Issued: 10,398)..£60
— Proof piedfort in silver *FDC* (Edition: 5,000).......................................£90
— Proof in gold *FDC* (Issued: 1,500)..£1800
— Proof piedfort in platinum *FDC* (Issued: 150)....................................£4000

L19 **Five pounds** (crown). Prince of Wales 60th Birthday. R. A profile portrait of His Royal Highness The Prince of Wales with the inscription 'THE PRINCE OF WALES' above and '1948 ICH DIEN 2008' below with the edge inscription 'SIXTIETH BIRTHDAY' on the precious metal versions. Obv. as 4556. (Reverse design : Ian Rank-Broadley)

2008...£7
— Specimen in presentation folder (Issued: 54,746)..................................£10
— Proof *FDC* (in 2008 set, see PS93)*...£15
— Proof in silver *FDC* (Issued: 7,446)...£60
— Proof piedfort in silver *FDC* (Edition: 5,000).......................................£90
— Proof in gold *FDC* (Issued: 867)..£1800
— Proof in platinum *FDC* (Issued: 54) £4000

* *Coins marked thus were originally issued in Royal Mint sets.*

L20   L21

L20   **Five pounds** (crown). 500th Anniversary of the accession of Henry VIII. R. A
design inspired By a Holbein painting of King Henry VIII, set within a tressure and
surrounded by the inscription 'THE ACCESSION OF HENRY VIII 1509' and the
denomination 'FIVE POUNDS', with the edge inscription 'ROSA SINE SPINA' on
the precious metal versions. Obv. as 4551. (Reverse design: John Bergdahl)

2009..£7
—   Specimen in presentation folder (Edition: 100,000) £10
—   Proof *FDC* (in 2009 set, see PS97)* £15
—   Proof in silver *FDC* (Issued: 10,419))...£60
—   Proof piedfort in silver *FDC* (Issued: 3,580) £90
—   Proof in gold *FDC* (Issued: 1,130)...£1800
—   Proof piedfort in platinum *FDC* (Edition: 100) £4500

L21   **Five pounds** (crown). Commemorating the three hundred-and fiftieth anniversary
of the restoration of the Monarchy. R. A design featuring a crown, a spray of oak
leaves, interlinked 'C's, the date '1660', the inscription 'RESTORATION OF THE
MONARCHY' and the denomination 'FIVE POUNDS' with the edge inscription 'A
QUIET AND PEACEFUL POSSESSION' on the precious metal versions. Obv. as
4551. (Reverse design: David Cornell)

2010..£7
—   Specimen on presentation card (Edition: 150,000) £8
—   Specimen in presentation folder (Edition: 50,000) £10
—   Proof *FDC* (in 2010 set, see PS101)* £15
—   Proof in silver *FDC* (Issued: 6,518)..£50
—   Proof piedfort in silver *FDC* (Issued: 4,435) £90
—   Proof in gold *FDC* (Issued: 1,182)...£1800
—   Proof piedfort in platinum *FDC* (Edition: 100) £4500

* Coins marked thus were originally issued in Royal Mint sets.

L22

L22 **Five pounds** (crown). Royal Wedding Commemorative. R.A design featuring facing portraits of His Royal Highness Prince William and Miss Catherine Middleton with the inscription 'WILLIAM AND CATHERINE' above and the date '29 APRIL 2011 below. (Reverse design: Mark Richards)

2011
- Specimen in presentation folder (Issued: 250,000) £18
- Proof in silver *FDC* (Issued: 26,069)..£75
- Proof in silver with gold plating *FDC* (Issued: 7,451) £90
- Proof piedfort in silver *FDC* (Issued: 2,991)..£120
- Proof in gold *FDC* (Issued: 2,066) £1800
- Proof piedfort in platinum *FDC* (Edition: 200)..£4500

L23

L23 **Five pounds** (crown). 90th Birthday of Prince Philip. R. A profile portrait of His Royal Highness The Duke of Edinburgh with the inscription 'PRINCE PHILIP 90TH BIRTHDAY ' and the denomination 'FIVE POUNDS' and the date '2011' (Reverse design: Mark Richards)

2011
- Specimen in presentation folder (Edition: 50,000)...£10
- Proof *FDC* (in 2011 set, see PS104)*..£15
- Proof in silver *FDC* (Issued: 4,599) £83
- Proof piedfort in silver *FDC* (Issued: 2,659)..£145
- Proof in gold *FDC* (Issued: 636) £1800
- Proof piedfort in platinum *FDC* (Edition: 90)...£4500

* Coins marked thus were originally issued in Royal Mint sets.

L24

L24 **Five pounds** (crown). Diamond Jubilee commemorative 2012. O. For the obverse impression, Our Effigy, inspired by the sculpture mounted in the entrance to the Supreme Court building on Parliament Square, with the inscription 'ELIZABETH. II. D. G. REG. F. D. FIVE POUNDS', and for the reverse an adaptation of Our Effigy first used on United Kingdom coins from 1953, with an olive branch and ribbon below, the date '2012' to the left and the inscription 'DIRIGE DEVS GRESSVS MEOS' to the right. With the edge inscription 'A VOW MADE GOOD' on the precious metal coins. (Obverse and reverse designs: Ian Rank-Broadley) 2012

— Specimen in presentation folder (Issued: 484,775 .... £13
— Proof *FDC* (in 2012 set, see PS107)* £10
— Proof in silver *FDC* (Issued: 16,370 including coins in sets) £83
— Proof in silver with gold plating *FDC* (Issued: 12,112) £100
— Proof piedfort in silver *FDC* (Issued: 3,187) £145
— Proof in gold *FDC* (Issued: 1,085) £2000
— Proof piedfort in platinum *FDC* (Issued: 20) £4500

L25

L25 **Five pounds** (crown). Coronation Anniversary commemorative 2013.R. In the centre The Imperial State Crown with the inscription 'TO REIGN AND SERVE' and 'A VOW MADE GOOD' (Reverse design: Emma Noble). 2013

— Specimen in presentation folder £13
— Proof *FDC* (in 2013 set, see PS109)* £10
— Proof in silver *FDC* (Issued: 4,050 including coins in sets) £80
— Proof in silver with gold plating *FDC* (Issued: 2,547) £100
— Proof piedfort in silver *FDC* (Issued: 2,686 including coins in sets) £160
— Proof in gold *FDC* (Issued: 418 including coins in sets) £2500
— Proof piedfort in platinum *FDC* (Issued: 106) £5000

* Coins marked thus were originally issued in Royal Mint sets.

L26

L26 Five pounds (crown). Commemorative coin to mark the birth of a son to the
Duke and Duchess of Cambridge. R. A depiction of St. George armed, sitting on
horseback, attacking the dragon with a sword, and a broken spear upon the ground,
and the date of the year.(Reverse design: Benedetto Pistrucci).
2013
— Proof in silver *FDC* (Issued: 7,460) £80

L27

L27 Five pounds (crown) Commemorative coin to mark the christening of Prince
George of Cambridge. R. A deconstructed silver lily font incorporating cherubs
and roses, with a Baroque-style cartouche with the inscription 'DIEU ET MON
DROIT' and ' TO CELEBRATE THE CHRISTENING OF PRINCE GEORGE OF
CAMBRIDGE 2013' in the centre of the coin. (Reverse design: John Bergdahl).
2013
— Specimen in presentation folder... £13
— Proof in silver *FDC* (Issued: 7,264)... £80
— Proof piedfort in silver *FDC* (Issued: 2,251) £160
— Proof in gold *FDC* (Issued: 486).. £2000
— Proof piedfort in platinum *FDC* (Issued: 38).. £5000

* Coins marked thus were originally issued in Royal Mint sets.

L28

L28 **Five pounds** (crown). Obverse design depicts the Royal Arms with the date '2013' below. R. The portrait of The Queen by Mary Gillick with the inscription 'ELIZABETH II DEI GRATIA REGINA F.D.' and the denomination 'FIVE POUNDS' below. (Obverse design: James Butler).

2013
— Proof in silver *FDC* (Issued: 1,465 in sets, see PSS53)* £100
— Proof piedfort in silver *FDC* (Issued: 697 in sets, see PSS54)* £200
— Proof in gold *FDC* (Issued: 148 in sets, see PGQPS)* £3000

L29

L29 **Five pounds** (crown). Obverse design depicts the Royal Arms with the date 2013' below. R. The portrait of The Queen by Arnold Machin with the inscription 'ELIZABETH II D: G REG: F: D: FIVE POUNDS'. (Obverse design: James Butler).

2013
— Proof in silver *FDC* (Issued: 1,465 in sets, see PSS53)* £100
— Proof piedfort in silver *FDC* (Issued: 697 in sets, see PSS54)* £200
— Proof in gold *FDC* (Issued: 148 in sets, see PGQPS)* £3000

* *Coins marked thus were originally issued in Royal Mint sets.*

L30 L31

L30 **Five pounds** (crown). Obverse design depicts the Royal Arms with the date '2013' below. R. The portrait of The Queen by Raphael Maklouf with the inscription 'ELIZABETH II DEI. GRATIA. REGINA. F. D.' and the denomination 'FIVE POUNDS' below. (Obverse design: James Butler).

2013

— Proof in silver *FDC* (Issued: 1,465 in sets, see PSS53)* £100
— Proof piedfort in silver *FDC* (Issued: 697 in sets, see PSS54)* £200
— Proof in gold *FDC* (Issued: 148 in sets, see PGQPS)* £3000

L31 **Five pounds** (crown). Obverse design depicts the Royal Arms with the date '2013' below. R. The portrait of The Queen by Ian Rank-Broadley with the inscription 'ELIZABETH II D. G. REG. F.D and the denomination 'FIVE POUNDS' below. (Obverse design: James Butler).

2013

— Proof in silver *FDC* (Issued: 1,465 in sets, see PSS53)* £100
— Proof piedfort in silver *FDC* (Issued: 697 in sets, see PSS54)* £200
— Proof in gold *FDC* (Issued: 148 in sets, see PGQPS)* £3000

L32

L32 **Five pounds** (crown). Queen Anne commemorative. R. The effigy pf Queen Anne enclosed by baroque decoration including the Royal Arms from the reign of Queen Anne and surrounded by the inscription 'QUEEN ANNE DEI GRATIA 1665-1714' (Reverse design: Mark Edwards).

2014

— Specimen in presentation folder... £13
— Proof *FDC* (in 2014 set, see PS112)* £10
— Proof in silver *FDC* (Edition: 60,000 including coins in sets)............................. £80
— Proof in silver with gold plating *FDC* (Edition: 5,114)..................................... £100
— Proof piedfort in silver *FDC* (Edition: 4,028 including coins in sets)............... £160
— Proof in gold *FDC* (Edition: 2,060 including coins in sets) £2500
— Proof piedfort in platinum *FDC* (Edition: 150) £4500

* Coins marked thus were originally issued in Royal Mint sets.

L33

L33 **Five pounds** (crown). Commemorative coin to mark the first birthday of Prince
George of Cambridge. R. The four Quarterings of Our Royal Arms each contained in
a shield and arranged in saltire with, in the intervening spaces, a Rose, a Thistle, both
slipped and leaved, a sprig of shamrock and a Leek, in the centre the Crown and in the
base the date of the year. (Reverse design: Edgar Fuller)
2014
— Proof in silver *FDC* (Edition: 7,500) £80

L34

L35

L34 **Five pounds** (crown). Celebrating British Landmarks. R. A design depicting the
head of one of the lions in Trafalgar Square with Nelson's Column in the background
and the inscription 'FIVE POUNDS' (Reverse design: Glyn Davies and Laura Clancy)
2014
— Proof in silver *FDC* with colour printing (Edition: 5,000 see PSS59)*

L35 **Five pounds** (crown). Celebrating British Landmarks. R. A design depicting a view
of the Elizabeth Tower with the inscription 'FIVE POUNDS' (Reverse design:
Glyn Davies and Laura Clancy)
2014
— Proof in silver *FDC* with colour printing (Edition: 5,000 see PSS59)*

* Coins marked thus were originally issued in Royal Mint sets.

L36   L37

L36 **Five pounds** (crown). Celebrating British Landmarks. R. A design depicting Tower Bridge with the inscription 'FIVE POUNDS' (Reverse design: Glyn Davies and Laura Clancy)
2014
— Proof in silver *FDC* with colour printing (Edition: 5,000 see PSS59)*

L37 **Five pounds** (crown). Celebrating British Landmarks. R. A design depicting the Victoria Memorial with Buckingham Palace in the background and the inscription 'FIVE POUNDS' (Reverse design: Glyn Davies and Laura Clancy)
2014
— Proof in silver *FDC* with colour printing (Edition: 5,000 see PSS59)*

L38

L38 **Five pounds.** (Crown) Fifth Anniversary of the death of Winston Churchill, R. A portrait of Winston Churchill with the inscription 'CHURCHILL' with the edge inscription on the precious metal versions 'NEVER FLINCH, NEVER WEARY, NEVER DESPAIR' (Reverse design: Mark Richards).
2015
— BU in presentation pack £13
— Proof *FDC* (in 2015 set, see PS115)* £5
— Proof in silver *FDC* (Edition: 10,875 including coins in sets) £80
— Proof piedfort in silver *FDC* (Edition: 4,150 including coins in sets)...................£160
— Proof in gold *FDC* (Edition: 770)...£1800
— Proof piedfort in platinum *FDC* (Edition: 90) £4500

L39

L39   Five pounds. (Crown) Bicentenary pf the Battle of Waterloo, R. A depiction of the
      Duke of Wellington greeting the Prussian General Gebhard Leberecht von Blucher
      after the Battle of Waterloo with the inscription 'THE BATTLE OF WATERLOO
      1815'with the edge inscription on the precious metal versions 'THE NEAREST RUN
      THING YOU EVER SAW' (Reverse design: David Lawrence).
      2015
      —   BU in presentation pack...£13
      —   Proof *FDC* (in 2015 set, see PS117)*..£5
      —   Proof in silver *FDC* (Edition: 3,000 see PSS63 and PSS64)...................................£80
      —   Proof piedfort in silver *FDC* (Edition: 1,500) £150
      —   Proof in gold *FDC* (Edition: 100)...£2500

Obverse portrait by Jody Clark

L39A

L39A Five pounds. (Crown) Bicentenary pf the Battle of Waterloo, R. A depiction of the
      Duke of Wellington greeting the Prussian General Gebhard Leberecht von Blucher
      after the Battle of Waterloo with the inscription 'THE BATTLE OF WATERLOO
      1815'with the edge Inscription on the precious metal versions 'THE NEAREST RUN
      THING YOU EVER SAW' (Reverse design David Lawrence)
      2015
      —   Proof in silver *FDC* (Edition: 3,000) £80
      —   Proof piedfort in silver *FDC* (Edition: 1,500) £160
      —   Proof in gold *FDC* (Edition: 500)...£1800

* Coins marked thus were originally issued in Royal Mint sets.

L40

L40 **Five pounds.** (Crown) The second child of The Duke and Duchess of Cambridge. R. An ornamental cartouche in the centre featuring the inscription 'THE DUKE AND DUCHESS OF CAMBRIDGE 2015' surrounded by the inscription 'TO CELEBRATE THE BIRTH OF THE SECOND CHILD' (Reverse design: John Bergdahl)

2015

— BU in presentation pack...£13
— Proof in silver *FDC* (Edition: 9,500)..£80
— Proof in gold *FDC* (Edition: 350)...£2000

L41　　　　　　　　　　　　L42

L41 **Five pounds.** (Crown) Commemorating the Christening of Princess Charlotte of Cambridge R. A design depicting a deconstructed silver lily font incorporating cherubs,with a Baroque - Style cartouche and 'DIEU ET – MON DROIT' below and in the centre the inscription 'TO CELEBRATE THE CHRISTENING OF PRINCESS CHARLOTTE ELIZABETH DIANA OF CAMBRIDGE 2015' (Reverse design: John Bergdahl)

2015

— BU in presentation pack...£13
— Proof in silver *FDC* (Edition: 5,000)..£80
— Proof in gold *FDC* (Edition: 350)...£2000

L42 **Five pounds.** (Crown) Prince George's second birthday. R. A design depicting St George slaying the dragon and the date '2015' (Reverse design: Christopher Le Brun)

2015

— Proof in silver *FDC* (Edition: 7,500)..£80

Obverse portrait by James Butler

L43

L43   **Five pounds.** (Crown) The Longest serving monarch.. R. St Edwards crown in the centre and the date '1952'and '2015' above and 'ONE CROWN' below with the edge inscription on the precious metal versions 'LONG TO REIGN OVER US' (Obverse and reverse designs: James Butler)
2015
- —   BU in presentation pack £13
- —   Proof in silver *FDC* (Edition:15,000) £80
- —   Proof piedfort in silver *FDC* (Edition: 4,200) £160
- —   Proof in gold *FDC* (Edition: 1,500) £2000
- —   Proof piedfort in platinum *FDC* (Edition: 88) £4500

Obverse portrait by Jody Clark

L44

L44   **Five pounds.** (Crown) 90th Birthday of Her Majesty Queen Elizabeth II. R. A crowned Royal Cypher above the number '90' encircled by roses with the edge inscription 'FULL OF HONOUR AND YEARS' on the precious metal versions. (Reverse design: Christopher Hobbs).
2016
- —   Specimen in presentation folder..£10
- —   Proof *FDC* (in 2016 set, see PS119)* £20
- —   Proof in silver *FDC* (Edition: 13,000) £80
- —   Proof piedfort in silver *FDC* (Edition: 7,000) £160
- —   Proof in gold *FDC* (Edition: 1,200) £2000
- —   Proof piedfort in platinum *FDC* (Edition: 90) £4500

L45   **L46**

L45 **Five pounds.** Celebrating British Landmarks. A depiction of The White Cliffs of Dover with the inscription 'WHITE CLIFFS OF DOVER'. (Reverse design: Glyn Davies and Laura Clancy)
2016 — Proof in silver *FDC* with colour printing.
(Edition: 3,500 including coins in sets, see PSS71)

L46 **Five pounds.** Celebrating British Landmarks. A depiction of the Giant's Causeway the inscription 'GIANT'S CAUSEWAY'. (Reverse design: Glyn Davies and Laura Clancy)
2016 — Proof in silver *FDC* with colour printing.
(Edition: 3,500 including coins in sets, see PSS71)

L47   **L48**

L47 **Five pounds.** Celebrating British Landmarks. A depiction of the Lake District with the inscription 'LAKE DISTRICT'. (Reverse design: Glyn Davies and Laura Clancy)
2016 — Proof in silver *FDC* with colour printing.
(Edition: 3,500 including coins in sets, see PSS71)

L48 **Five pounds.** Celebrating British Landmarks. A depiction of Snowdonia with the inscription 'SNOWDONIA'. (Reverse design: Glyn Davies and Laura Clancy)
2016 — Proof in silver *FDC* with colour printing.
(Edition: 3,500 including coins in sets, see PSS71)

Obverse portrait by Ian Rank Broadley

M1

M1   **Ten pounds** (five ounce). Diamond Jubilee commemorative 2012. O. For the obverse
impression, Our Effigy, inspired by the sculpture mounted in the entrance to the
Supreme Court building on Parliament Square, with the inscription 'ELIZABETH.
II. D. G. REG. F. D. TEN POUNDS', and for the reverse an enthroned representation
of Ourself surrounded by the inscription 'DILECTA REGNO MCMLII – MMXII'
(Obverse and reverse design: Ian Rank-Broadley)
2012
— Proof in silver *FDC* (Issued: 1,933)..£350
— Proof in gold *FDC* (Issued: 140)..£7500
Illustration shown at reduced size – actual coin diameter 65 mm.

M2

M2   **Ten pounds** (five ounce). Coronation Anniversary. R. In the foreground the Orb and
Sceptre resting upon the Coronation Robe with the arches of Westminster Abbey
in the background with the inscription 'HER MAJESTY QUEEN ELIZABETH II
CORONATION ANNIVERSARY' (Reverse design: Jonathan Olliffe).
2013
— Proof in silver (0.999) *FDC* (Issued: 1,604) £450
— Proof in gold (0.9999) *FDC* (Issued: 74) £7500
Illustration shown at reduced size – actual coin diameter 63mm

M3

M3 **Ten pounds** (five ounce) Commemorative coin to mark the christening of Prince George of Cambridge. R. A deconstructed silver lily font incorporating cherubs and roses, with a Baroque-style cartouche with the inscription 'DIEU ET MON DROIT' and ' TO CELEBRATE THE CHRISTENING OF PRINCE GEORGE OF CAMBRIDGE 2013' in the centre of the coin. (Reverse design: John Bergdahl).
2013
—   Proof in silver (0.999) *FDC* (Issued: 912) £450
—   Proof in gold (0.9999) *FDC* (Issued: 48) £7500
Illustration shown at reduced size – actual coin diameter 63mm

M4

M4 **Ten pounds** (five ounce). 100th Anniversary of the outbreak of the First World War. R. A depiction of a lion behind the figure of Britannia holding a shield and a trident, watching over departing ships from a cliff top, with the inscription 'THE FIRST WORLD WAR 1914 1918' and the date at the base of the coin. (0.999 fine silver.) (Reverse design: John Bergdahl)
2014
—   Proof in silver (0.999) *FDC* (Edition: 1,300).. £395
—   Proof in gold (0.9999) *FDC* (Edition: 100).. £7500

M5

M5   **Ten pounds** (five ounce). Churchill R. A depiction of Sir Winston Churchill with the inscription 'CHURCHILL' at the base of the coin. (Reverse design: Etienne Millner) 2015
-   Proof on silver *FDC* (5 oz. fine silver) (Edition: 900)..£395
-   Proof in gold *FDC* (5 oz. fine gold) (Edition: 60) £7,500

Obverse portrait by Jody Clark

M6

M6   **Ten pounds** (five ounce). World War One. R.A depiction of the landscape of the Western Front with the inscription '1914 – 1918' Reverse design: James Butler) 2015
-   Proof on silver *FDC* (5 oz. fine silver) (Edition: 500)..£395
-   Proof in gold *FDC* (5 oz. fine gold) (Edition: 50) £7500

M7

M7 **Ten pounds** (five ounce). Commemorating the Christening of Princess Charlotte of Cambridge R. A design depicting a deconstructed silver lily font incorporating cherubs, with a Baroque-Style cartouche and 'DIEU ET – MON DROIT' below and in the centre the inscription 'TO CELEBRATE THE CHRISTENING OF PRINCESS CHARLOTTE ELIZABETH DIANA OF CAMBRIDGE 2015' (Reverse design: John Bergdahl) 2015

— Proof in silver *FDC* £400

Obverse portrait by James Butler

M8

M8 **Ten pounds** (five ounce). The Longest serving monarch R. A design depicting Our Royal Cypher below Our five definitive coinage portraits and the inscription 'THE LONGEST REIGN'.(Reverse design: Stephen Taylor) 2015

— Proof on silver *FDC* (5 oz. fine silver) (Edition: 1,500).......................................£395
— Proof in gold *FDC* (5 oz. fine gold) (Edition: 180) £7500

Obverse portrait by Jody Clark

M9

M9   Ten pounds. (Five ounce). R. In the centre a depiction of William Shakespeare
accompanied with the inscription 'OTHELLO ACT 1 SC 3' surrounded by the
inscription 'PUT MONEY IN THY PURSE' 2016'. (Reverse design: Tom Phillips)
2016
—   Proof in silver *FDC* (Edition: 750) £395
—   Proof on gold *FDC* (Edition: 50) £6,950
Illustration shown at reduced size – actual coin diameter 65mm

M10

M10   Ten pounds. (Five ounce). 90th Birthday of Her Majesty Queen Elizabeth II. R. A
crowned Royal Cypher above the number '90' encircled by roses.. (Reverse design:
Christopher Hobbs).
2016
—   Proof in silver *FDC* (Edition: 1,750) £395
—   Proof in gold *FDC* (Edition: 170) £7500
Illustration shown at reduced size – actual coin diameter 65mm

Obverse portrait by Ian Rank-Broadley

N1

N1 **Twenty pounds.** R. A depiction of St. George armed, sitting on horseback, attacking
the dragon with a sword, and a broken spear upon the ground and the date of the
year. (0.999 fine silver) (Reverse design: Benedetto Pistrucci).
2013
—   Silver BU (Issued: 250,000)..£20

N2

N2 **Twenty pounds.** R. A depiction of a lion behind the figure of Britannia holding
a shield and a trident, watching over departing ships from a cliff top, with the
inscription 'THE FIRST WORLD WAR 1914 1918' and the date at the base of the
coin. (0.999 fine silver) (Reverse design: John Bergdahl)
2014
—   Silver BU (Edition: 250,000) £20

Obverse portrait by Jody Clark

N3   N4

N3 **Twenty pounds.** Churchill R. A depiction of Sir Winston Churchill with the
inscription 'CHURCHILL' at the base of the coin. (Reverse design: Etienne Millner)
2015
—   Silver BU (Edition : 200,000)

N4 **Twenty pounds.** The Longest serving monarch. R. A design depicting Our Royal
Cypher below Our five definitive coinage portraits and the inscription 'THE
LONGEST REIGN' (Reverse design: Stephen Taylor)
2015
—   Silver BU (Edition: 150,000)..£20

Obverse portrait by Jody Clark

N5

N5 **Twenty pounds.** 90th Birthday of Her Majesty Queen Elizabeth II. R. A crowned
Royal Cypher above the number '90' encircled by roses (Reverse design:
Christopher Hobbs).
2016 —   Silver BU (Edition: 150,000)..£20

N6

N6 **Twenty pounds.** R. A dragon with the inscription 'TWENTY POUNDS' (Reverse
design: Norman Sillman)
2016 —   Silver BU (Edition: 150,000)..£20

N7

N7 Twenty pounds. R. A depiction of Mary and the baby Jesus receiving gifts from
the Magi, with the inscription 'THE NATIVITY: CHRISTMAS 2016'.
2016 —   Silver BU (Edition: 30,000) £20

P1 **One hundred pounds.** World War I R. A depiction of Lord Kitchener pointing above the inscription 'YOUR COUNTRY NEEDS YOU' and the inscription 'THE FIRST WORLD WAR 1914-1918' and the date '2014' surrounding the design. (Reverse design: John Bergdahl).
2014
— Proof in Platinum *FDC*

Obverse portrait by Ian Rank-Broadley

P2

P2 **One hundred pounds.** Elizabeth Tower (Reverse design: Glyn Davies and Laura Clancy)
2015
— Silver BU (Edition: 50,000) £100

Obverse portrait by Jody Clark

P3

P3 **One hundred pounds.** R. A design the Victoria Memorial with Buckingham Palace in the background Reverse design: Glyn Davies and Laura Clancy)
2015
— Silver BU (Issued: 50,000)..£100

P4

P4   **One hundred pound.** (Two oz fine silver). R. A view of Trafalgar Square with the head
of a lion in the foreground and Nelson Column in the background. (Reverse design: Laura
Clancy and Glyn Davies)
2016
—   Silver BU (Edition: 45,000) £100

Obverse portrait by Ian Rank-Broadley

Q1

Q1   **Five hundred pounds** (one kilo). Diamond Jubilee commemorative 2012. O. For the
obverse impression, Our Effigy, inspired by the sculpture mounted in the entrance to the
Supreme Court building on Parliament Square, with the inscription 'ELIZABETH. II. D.
G. REG. F. D. 500 POUNDS', and for the reverse a full achievement of the Royal Arms
based on those mounted on the front gates of Buckingham Palace with the date '2012'
below. (Obverse and reverse design: Ian Rank-Broadley)
2012
—   Proof in silver *FDC* (Issued: 206)..£2000
Illustration shown at reduced size – actual coin diameter 100 mm.

Q2   **Five hundred pounds** (one kilo). R. Coronation commemorative 2013. R. In the
foreground the Orb and Sceptre with the St. Edward's Crown behind surrounding
by flowers representing the constituent parts of the United Kingdom and in the
background a ribbon showing the '2nd JUNE 1953' with the inscription 'QUEEN
ELIZABETH II' and 'THE 60TH ANNIVERSARY OF THE CORONATION'
(Reverse design: John Bergdahl)
2013
—   Proof in silver *FDC* (0.999) (Issued: 301))..£2600

Q3

Q3 **Five hundred pounds.** (1 kilo of fine silver). Commemorative coin to mark the
christening of Prince George of Cambridge. R. A deconstructed silver lily font
incorporating cherubs and roses, with a Baroque-style cartouche with the inscription
'DIEU ET MON DROIT' and 'TO CELEBRATE THE CHRISTENING OF PRINCE
GEORGE OF CAMBRIDGE 2013'in the centre of the coin. (Reverse design: John
Bergdahl).
2013
— Proof in silver (0.999) *FDC* (Issued: 194)).. £2000
Illustration shown at reduced size – actual coin diameter 100mm

Q4

Q4 **Five hundred pounds.** (1 kilo of fine silver). World War 1. R. A design depicting
British soldiers marching through no man's land with the figure of a British soldier
with rifle and helmet in the foreground and the dates '1914-1918' at the base of the coin.
(Reverse design: Michael Sandle).
2014
— Proof in silver (0.999) *FDC* (Edition: 430)..£2000
Illustration shown at reduced size – actual coin diameter 100mm

Obverse portrait by James Butler

Q5

Q5 **Five hundred pounds.** (1 kilo of fine silver).The Longest serving monarch R. A design depicting Our Royal Cypher below Our five definitive coinage portraits and the inscription 'THE LONGEST REIGN'. (Reverse design: Stephen Taylor) 2015
— Proof on silver *FDC* (Edition: 320) £2000
Illustration shown at reduced size – actual coin diameter 100mm

Obverse portrait by Jody Clark

Q6

Q6 **Five hundred pounds.** (1 kilo of fine silver). 90th Birthday of Her Majesty Queen Elizabeth II. R. A crowned Royal Cypher above the number '90' encircled by roses with the inscription 'FULL OF HONOUR AND YEARS'. (Reverse design: Christopher Hobbs).
2016
— Proof in silver *FDC* (Edition: 450) £2000
Illustration shown at reduced size – actual coin diameter 100mm

Q7

Q7 **Five hundred pounds.** (Five ounce) Commemorating the Christening of Princess Charlotte of Cambridge. R. A design depicting a deconstructed silver lily font incorporating cherubs, with a Baroque Style cartouche and 'DIEU ET – MON DROIT' below and in the centre the inscription 'TO CELEBRATE THE CHRISTENING OF PRINCESS CHARLOTTE ELIZABETH DIANA OF CAMBRIDGE 2015'. (Reverse design: John Bergdàhl)
2015 —   Proof in gold *FDC* £7500

<table>
<tr><td align="center">R1</td><td align="center">R3</td></tr>
</table>

R1 **One thousand pounds** (one kilo). Diamond Jubilee commemorative 2012. O. For the obverse impression, Our Effigy, inspired by the sculpture mounted in the entrance to the Supreme Court building on Parliament Square, with the inscription 'ELIZABETH. II. D. G. REG. F. D. 1000 POUNDS', and for the reverse a full achievement of the Royal Arms based on those mounted on the front gates of Buckingham Palace with the date '2012' below. (Reverse design:
2012 —   Proof in gold *FDC* (Issued: 21)) £55000
Illustration shown at reduced size – actual coin diameter 100mm

R2 **One thousand pounds** (One kilo). Coronation commemorative 2013. R. In the foreground the Orb and Sceptre with the St. Edward's Crown behind surrounding by flowers representing the constituent parts of the United Kingdom and in the background a ribbon showing the '2nd JUNE 1953' with the inscription 'QUEEN ELIZABETH II' and 'THE 60TH ANNIVERSARY OF THE CORONATION' (Reverse design: John Bergdahl)
2013 —   Proof in gold *FDC* (0.9999) (Issued: 13)) £55000

R3 One thousand pounds (1 kilo of fine gold). Commemorative coin to mark the christening of Prince George of Cambridge. R. A deconstructed silver lily font incorporating cherubs and roses, with a Baroque-style cartouche with the inscription 'DIEU ET MON DROIT' and 'TO CELEBRATE THE CHRISTENING OF PRINCE GEORGE OF CAMBRIDGE 2013'in the centre of the coin. (Reverse design: John Bergdahl).
2013 —   Proof in gold *FDC* (0.9999) (Issued: 19) £55000
Illustration shown at reduced size – actual coin diameter 100mm

R4

R4   **One thousand pounds.** (1 kilo of fine gold). World War 1. R. A design depicting
British soldiers marching through no man's land with the figure of a British soldier
with rifle and helmet in the foreground and the dates '1914-1918' at the base of the coin.
(Reverse design: Michael Sandle).
2014
—   Proof in gold *FDC* (0.9999) (Edition: 25)..£55000
Illustration shown at reduced size – actual coin diameter 100mm

R5

R5   **One thousand pounds.** (1 kilo of fine gold) The Longest serving monarch.
R. A design depicting Our Royal Cypher below Our five definitive coinage portraits
and the inscription 'THE LONGEST REIGN'. (Reverse design: Stephen Taylor)
2015
—   Proof in gold *FDC* £55000
Illustration shown at reduced size – actual coin diameter 100mm

R6

R6   **One thousand pounds.** (1 kilo of fine gold). 90th Birthday of Her Majesty Queen
Elizabeth II. R. A crowned Royal Cypher above the number '90' encircled by roses with
the inscription 'FULL OF HONOUR AND YEARS'. Reverse design:
Christopher Hobbs).
2016
—   Proof in gold *FDC* (Edition: 25) £55000
Illustration shown at reduced size – actual coin diameter 100mm

Obverse portrait by Ian Rank-Broadley

SA1   SA2

SA1   **Quarter sovereign.** R. The image of St George armed, sitting on horseback, attacking the dragon with a sword, and a broken spear upon the ground, and the date of the year. (Reverse design: Benedetto Pistrucci)

2009 Bullion type (Edition: 50,000)...£110
—   Proof *FDC* (Issued: 13,495 including coins in sets) £125
2010 Bullion type (Edition: 250,000)..£110
—   Proof *FDC* (Issued: 6,007 including coins in sets) £125
2011 Bullion type (Edition: 50,000)..£110
—   Proof *FDC* (Issued: 7,764 including coins in sets) £125
2013 Bullion type
—   Proof *FDC* (Issued: 1,729)*
2014 Bullion type
—   Proof *FDC* (Issued: 1,696 including coins in sets)* £125
2015
—   Proof (Edition: 4,600 including coins in sets)...£125

SA2   **Quarter sovereign.** R. The image of St George on horseback, attacking the dragon with a lance, with date of the year to the left. (Reverse design: Paul Day)

2012 Bullion type (Edition: 250,000) £80
—   Proof *FDC* (Issued: 7,579)...£150

Obverse portrait by Jody Clark

SA3

SA3   **Quarter sovereign.**

2015 Proof *FDC* (Edition: 4,600 including coins in sets) £125

Obverse portrait by James Butler

SA4

SA4   **Quarter Sovereign.** R. St George and Dragon.

2016
—   Proof *FDC* (Edition: 4,575 including coins in sets)..£125

* Coins marked thus were originally issued in Royal Mint sets.

Obverse portrait by Jody Clark

SA5

SA5 Quarter Sovereign. R. The image of St George armed, sitting on horseback, attacking the dragon with a broken spear surrounded by the inscription 'HONI SOIT QUI MAL Y PENSE'. 2017
— Proof *FDC* (Edition: 5,100 including coins in sets)..£145

Obverse portrait by Arnold Machin

SB1

SB1 Half-sovereign. R. The image of St George armed, sitting on horseback, attacking the dragon with a sword, and a broken spear upon the ground, and the date of the year. (Reverse design: Benedetto Pistrucci)

1980 Proof *FDC* (Issued: 76.700). £180   1983 Proof *FDC* (Issued: 19,710)** £180
1982 Unc ....£150   1984 Proof *FDC* (Issued: 12,410) £180
— Proof *FDC* (Issued: 19,090).. £180

Obverse portrait by Raphael Maklouf

SB2   SB3

SB2 Half-sovereign. R. St. George (as 4205)

1985 Proof *FDC* (Issued: 9,951)... £180   1992 Proof *FDC* (Issued: 3,783) £180
1986 Proof *FDC* (Issued: 4,575)... £180   1993 Proof *FDC* (Issued: 2,910) £180
1987 Proof *FDC* (Issued: 8,187)... £180   1994 Proof *FDC* (Issued: 5,000) £180
1988 Proof *FDC* (Issued: 7,074)... £180   1995 Proof *FDC* (Issued: 4,900) £180
1990 Proof *FDC* (Issued: 4,231)... £180   1996 Proof *FDC* (Issued: 5,730) £180
1991 Proof *FDC* (Issued: 3,588)... £180   1997 Proof *FDC* (Issued: 7,500) £180

SB3 Half-sovereign 500th Anniversary of Sovereign. For the obverse impression a representation Of Ourself as at Our Coronation, seated in King Edward's Chair and having received the Sceptre with the Cross and the Rod with the Dove, all within the circumscription 'ELIZABETH. II.DEI.GRA.REG.FID.DEF' and for the reverse a Shield of Our Royal Arms ensigned by an open Royal Crown, the whole superimposed upon a double Rose, and with the circumscription 'ANNIVERSARY OF THE GOLD SOVEREIGN 1489-1989' (Designs: Bernald Sindall)

1989 Proof *FDC* (Issued: 8,888)..£500

* *Coins marked thus were originally issued in Royal Mint sets.*
** *Numbers include coins sold in sets*

Obverse portrait by Ian Rank-Broadley

SB4   SB5   SB6

SB4 **Half sovereign.** R. St.George

1998 Proof *FDC* (Issued: 6,147)... £180   2004 Bullion type (Issued: 34,924) £150
1999 Proof *FDC* (Issued: 7,500)... £180   —   Proof *FDC* (Issued: 4,446) £180
2000 Bullion type (Issued: 146,822). £150   2006 Bullion type £150
—   Proof *FDC* (Issued: 7,458).... £180   —   Proof *FDC* (Issued: 4,173) £180
2001 Bullion type (Issued: 94,763) .£150   2007 Bullion type (Edition: 75,000)........£150
—   Proof *FDC* (Issued: 4,596).... £180   —   Proof *FDC* (Issued: 2,442) £180
2003 Bullion type (Issued: 47,818)£150   2008 Bullion type (Edition: 75,000)........£150
—   Proof *FDC* (Issued: 4,868).... £180   —   Proof *FDC* (Issued: 2,465) £180

SB5 **Half sovereign** R. The Shield of Arms of Our United Kingdom of Great Britain and Northern Ireland within an open wreath of laurel and ensigned by Our Royal Crown and beneath the date of the year. (Reverse design: Timothy Noad)

2002 Bullion type (Issued: 61,347)...£200
—   Proof *FDC* (Issued: 10,000)..£300

SB6 **Half sovereign.** R. A depiction of St George, carrying a shield and a sword, slaying the dragon, with the date '2005' beneath the wing of the dragon. (Reverse design: Timothy Noad)

2005 Bullion type (Issued: 30,299)..£200
—   Proof *FDC* (Issued: 5,011)..£300

SB7

SB7 **Half sovereign.** R. St George. Based on the original design of 1893 with reduced ground below design and larger exergue with no BP initials

2009 Bullion type (Edition: 50,000)..£165
—   Proof *FDC* (Issued: 5,412 including coins in sets) £225
2010 Bullion type (Edition: 250,000)..£165
—   Proof *FDC* (Issued: 5,370 including coins in sets) £225
2011 Bullion type (Edition: 50,000)..£160
—   Proof *FDC* (Issued 5,287 including coins in sets)..£225
2013 Bullion type (Issued: 1,051)
—   BU (Issued: 124 in sets, see PGS70)
—   Proof *FDC* (Issued: 1,863 including coins in sets)*
2014 Bullion type
—   BU (Edition: 9,900)..£170
—   Proof *FDC* (Edition: 4,075 including coins in sets)..£225
2015
—   BU (Edition: 5,000)..£175
—   Proof (Edition: 4,600 including coins in sets)...£250

* Coins marked thus were originally issued in Royal Mint sets.

SB7A Half sovereign. R. St George as SB7 above but with 'I' mint mark on reverse for coins
struck in India.
2014

SB8

SB8 Half sovereign. R. The image of St George on horseback, attacking the dragon with
a lance, with date of the year to the left. (Reverse design: Paul Day)
2012 Bullion type (Edition: 250,000)..£200
— Proof *FDC* (Issued: 2,303 ....£260

Obverse portrait by Jody Clark
SB9 Half sovereign. St George and dragon.
— 2015 Proof *FDC* (Edition: 1,100)..£250
— 2016 BU (Edition: 1,000) £195

Obverse portrait by James Butler

SB10

SB10 Half sovereign. R. St George and Dragon.
2016
— Proof *FDC* (Edition: 3,675 including coins in sets) £300

Obverse portrait by Jody Clark

SB11

SB11 Half sovereign. R. The image of St George armed, sitting on horseback, attacking the dragon
with a broken spear surrounded by the inscription 'HONI SOIT QUI MAL Y PENSE'.
2017
— Proof *FDC* (Edition: 5,150 including coins in sets)..£245

Obverse portrait by Arnold Machin

SC1

SC1   **Sovereign.** R. The image of St George armed, sitting on horseback, attacking the dragon with a sword, and a broken spear upon the ground, and the date of the year. (Reverse design: Benedetto Pistrucci)

1974 Unc	£280	1981 Unc	£280
1976 Unc	£280	— Proof *FDC* (Issued: 32,960)	£380
1976 VIP Proof *FDC*	*Extremely rare*	1982 Unc	£280
1978 Unc	£280	— Proof *FDC* (Issued: 20,000)	£380
1979 Unc	£280	1983 Proof *FDC* (Issued: 21,250)**	£380
— Proof *FDC* (Issued: 50,000)	£380	1984 Proof *FDC* (Issued: 12,880)	£380
1980 Unc	£280		
— Proof *FDC* (Issued: 81,200)	£380		

Obverse portrait by Raphael Maklouf

SC2   SC3

SC2   **Sovereign.** R. St. George (as 4204)

1985 Proof *FDC* (Issued: 11,393)	£380	1992 Proof *FDC* (Issued: 4,772)	£400
1986 Proof *FDC* (Issued: 5,079)	£380	1993 Proof *FDC* (Issued: 4,349)	£400
1987 Proof *FDC* (Issued: 9,979)	£380	1994 Proof *FDC* (Issued: 4,998)	£400
1988 Proof *FDC* (Issued: 7,670)	£380	1995 Proof *FDC* (Issued: 7,500)	£380
1990 Proof *FDC* (Issued: 4,767)	£380	1996 Proof *FDC* (Issued: 7,500)	£380
1991 Proof *FDC* (Issued: 4,713)	£380	1997 Proof *FDC* (Issued: 7,500)	£380

SC3   **Sovereign.** 500th Anniversary of Sovereign. For the obverse impression a representation Of Ourself as at Our Coronation, seated in King Edward's Chair and having received the Sceptre with the Cross and the Rod with the Dove, all within the circumscription 'ELIZABETH.II.DEI.GRA.REG.FID.DEF' and for the reverse a Shield of Our Royal Arms ensigned by an open Royal Crown, the whole superimposed upon a double Rose, and with the circumscription 'ANNIVERSARY OF THE GOLD SOVEREIGN 1489-1989' (Designs: Bernald Sindall)

1989 Proof *FDC* (Issued: 10,535) £1400

* Coins marked thus were originally issued in Royal Mint sets.
** Numbers include coins sold in sets

Obverse portrait by Ian Rank-Broadley

SC4

SC4 Sovereign. R. St.George

1998 Proof *FDC* (Issued: 10,000). £380

1999 Proof *FDC* (Issued: 10,000). £380

2000 Bullion type (Issued: 129,069).£280

— Proof *FDC* (Issued: 9,909).... £380

2001 Bullion type (Issued: 49,462)£280

— Proof *FDC* (Issued: 8,915).... £380

2003 Bullion type (Issued: 43,230)£280

— Proof *FDC* (Issued: 12,433).. £380

2004 Bullion type (Issued: 30,688) £280

— Proof *FDC* (Issued: 10,175) £380

2006 Bullion type £280

— Proof *FDC* (Issued: 9,195) £380

2007 Bullion type (Edition: 75,000)........£280

— Proof *FDC* (Issued: 8,199) £380

2008 Bullion type (Edition: 75,000)........£280

— Proof *FDC* (Edition: 12,500)...........£380

SC5   SC7

SC5 Sovereign R. The Shield of Arms of Our United Kingdom of Great Britain and Northern Ireland within an open wreath of laurel and ensigned by Our Royal Crown and beneath the date of the year. (Reverse design: Timothy Noad)

2002 Bullion type (Issued: 75,264)..£330

— Proof *FDC* (Issued: 12,500)...£500

SC6 Sovereign R. A depiction of St George, carrying a shield and a sword, slaying the dragon, with the date '2005' beneath the wing of the dragon.(Reverse design: Timothy Noad)

2005 Bullion type (Issued: 45,542)..£330

— Proof *FDC* (Issued: 12,500)...£450

SC7 Sovereign. R. St George. Based on the original design of 1820 with the plumed helmet without its streamer.

2009 Bullion type (Edition: 75,000)...£325

— Proof *FDC* (Issued: 9,770 including coins in sets)..£400

2010 Bullion type (Edition: 250,000)...£325

— Proof *FDC* (Issued: 8,828 including coins in sets)..£400

2011 Bullion type (Edition: 250,000)...£325

— Proof *FDC* (Edition: 15,000 including coins in sets) £400

2013 Bullion type (Issued: 2,695)

— BU (Issued: 124 in sets, see PGS70)..£325

— Proof *FDC* (Issued: 8,243 including coins in sets)..£400

2014 Bullion type

— BU (Edition: 15,000)..£325

— Proof *FDC* (Edition: 9,725 including coins in sets) £400

2015

— BU (Edition: 10,000)

— Proof (Edition : 9,800 including coins in sets) £450

Where numbers of coins issued or the Edition limit is quoted, these refer to individual coins. Additional coins were included in sets which are listed in the appropriate section.

SC7A Sovereign. R. St George as SC7 above but with 'I' mint mark on reverse for coins struck in India.

　　　2013 BU

SC8

SC8 Sovereign. R. The image of St George on horseback, attacking the dragon with a lance, with date of the year to the left. (Reverse design: Paul Day)

　　　2012 Bullion type (Edition: 250,000)..£330

　　　— Proof *FDC* (Issued: 5,501))..£600

Obverse portrait by Ian Rank- Broadley

SC9　Sovereign.

　　　2015

　　　— BU (Edition ; 10,000)

Obverse portrait by Jody Clark

SC10

SC10　Sovereign.

　　　2015

　　　— BU (Edition ; 10,000)

　　　— Proof *FDC* (Edition :8,800 including coins in sets) £500

　　　2016

　　　— BU (Edition: 1,500) £360

Obverse portrait by James Butler

SC11

SC11　Sovereign. R. St George and Dragon.

　　　2016

　　　— Proof *FDC* (Edition :9,675 including coins in sets) £500

Obverse portrait by Jody Clark

SC12

SC12 Sovereign. R. The image of St George armed, sitting on horseback, attacking the dragon
with a broken spear surrounded by the inscription 'HONI SOIT QUI MAL Y PENSE'.
2017
— Proof *FDC* (Edition: 13,500 including coins in sets)..£430

Obverse portrait by Arnold Machin

SD1

SD1 Two pounds R. The image of St George armed, sitting on horseback, attacking the dragon
with a sword, and a broken spear upon the ground, and the date of the year.(Reverse design:
Benedetto Pistrucci)
1980 Proof *FDC* (see PGS01)* ....£600   1983 Proof *FDC* (Issued: 12,500) ** £600
1982 Proof *FDC* (see PGS03)*.........£600

Obverse portrait by Raphael Maklouf

SD2

SD2 Two pounds. R. St. George
1985 Proof *FDC* (see PGS06)*.........£600   1991 Proof *FDC* (Issued: 620) £600
1987 Proof *FDC* (Issued: 1,801).......£600   1992 Proof *FDC* (Issued: 476) £600
1988 Proof *FDC* (Issued: 1,551).......£600   1993 Proof *FDC* (Issued: 414) £600
1990 Proof *FDC* (Issued: 716) ....£600   1996 Proof *FDC* (see PGS24)* £600

* Coins marked thus were originally issued in Royal Mint sets.
** Numbers include coins sold in sets

SD3

SD3 **Two pounds** 500th Anniversary of Sovereign. For the obverse impression a representation Of Ourself as at Our Coronation, seated in King Edward's Chair and having received the Sceptre with the Cross and the Rod with the Dove, all within the circumscription 'ELIZABETH. II.DEI.GRA.REG.FID.DEF' and for the reverse a Shield of Our Royal Arms ensigned by an open Royal Crown, the whole superimposed upon a double Rose, and with the circumscription 'ANNIVERSARY OF THE GOLD SOVEREIGN 1489-1989' (Designs: Bernald Sindall) 1989 Proof *FDC* (Issued: 2,000) £900

Obverse portrait by Ian Rank-Broadley

SD4

SD4 **Two pounds.** R. St. George

1998 Proof *FDC* (see PGS28)* £600	2000 Proof *FDC* (see PGS32)* £600
2003 Proof *FDC* (see PGS38)* £600	2006 Proof *FDC* (see PGS44)* £600
2007 Proof *FDC* (see PGS46)* £600	2008 Proof *FDC* (see PGS49)* £600

* Coins marked thus were originally issued in Royal Mint sets.

SD5 SD6 SD7

SD5 **Two pounds.** R. The Shield of Arms of Our United Kingdom of Great Britain and Northern Ireland within an open wreath of laurel and ensigned by Our Royal Crown and beneath the date of the year. (Reverse design: Timothy Noad)
2002 Proof *FDC* (see PGS36)*..£700

SD6 **Two pounds.** R. A depiction of St George, carrying a shield and a sword, slaying the dragon, with the date '2005' beneath the wing of the dragon.(Reverse design: Timothy Noad)
2005 Proof *FDC* (see PGS42)*..£700

SD7 **Two pounds.** R. St George. Based on the original design of 1820 with greater detail on the dragon.
2009 Proof *FDC* (see PGS52)*..£600
2010 Proof *FDC* (Edition: 2,750 in sets)* £600
2011 Proof *FDC* (Edition: 2,950 in sets)* £600
2013 BU (Issued: 124 in sets, see PGS70) £900
— Proof *FDC* (Edition: 1,895 in sets)*
2014 BU (Edition: 1,300)..£650
— Proof *FDC* (Edition:　　)
2015 Proof *FDC* (Edition: 1,100 including coins in sets).........................£750

SD8

SD8 **Two pounds.** R. The image of St George on horseback, attacking the dragon with a lance, with date of the year to the left. (Reverse design: Paul Day)
2012 BU (Edition: 60 in three coin set, see PGS6)*...................................£800
— Proof *FDC* (Edition: 1,944 including coins in sets)*

* Coins marked thus were originally issued in Royal Mint sets.

Obverse portrait by Jody Clark
SD9   Two pounds.
    2015 Proof *FDC* (Edition: 1,100 including coins in sets) £850

Obverse portrait by James Butler

SD10

SD10 Two pounds. R. St George and Dragon.
    2016
    —   Proof *FDC* (Edition: 925 including coins in sets)..£850

Obverse portrait by Jody Clark

SD11

SD11 Two pounds R. The image of St George armed, sitting on horseback, attacking the
    dragon with a broken spear surrounded by the inscription 'HONI SOIT QUI MAL Y
    PENSE'.
    2017
    —   Proof *FDC* (Edition: 1,200 in sets)

* Coins marked thus were originally issued in Royal Mint sets.

Obverse portrait by Arnold Machin

SE1

SE1   **Five pounds.** R. The image of St George armed, sitting on horseback, attacking the dragon
with a sword, and a broken spear upon the ground, and the date of the year.(Reverse
design: Benedetto Pistrucci)

1980 Proof *FDC* (see PGS01)*... £1800	1982 Proof *FDC* (see PGS03)*.............. £2250
1981 Proof *FDC* (Issued: 5,400)** £1800	1984 Proof *FDC* (Issued: 905)............... £1800

SE2   As 4201 but, 'U' in a circle to left of date

1984 (Issued: 15,104) *Unc* £1600

Obverse portrait by Raphael Maklouf

SE3   SE5

SE3   **Five pounds.** R. St. George.

1985 Proof *FDC* (see PGS06)*... £1650	1990 Proof *FDC* (see PGS12)*.............. £1650
1991 Proof *FDC* (see PGS14)*... £1650	1992 Proof *FDC* (see PGS16)*.............. £1650
1993 Proof *FDC* (see PGS18)*... £1650	1994 Proof *FDC* (see PGS20)*.............. £1650
1995 Proof *FDC* (see PGS22)*... £1650	1996 Proof *FDC* (see PGS24)*.............. £1650
1997 Proof *FDC* (see PGS26)*.. £1650	

SE4   **Five pounds** R. St George, 'U' in a circle to left of date.

1985 (Issued: 13,626).................. £1500	1993 (Issued: 906).................................. £1500
1986 (Issued: 7,723).................... £1500	1994 (Issued: 1,000).............................. £1500
1990 (Issued: 1,226)................... £1500	1995 (Issued: 1,000).............................. £1500
1991 (Issued: 976)....................... £1500	1996 (Issued: 901)................................. £1500
1992 (Issued: 797)....................... £1500	1997 (Issued: 802)................................. £1500

SE5   **Five pounds** Uncouped portrait of Queen Elizabeth II. As illustration. R. St. George, 'U'
in a circle to left of date.

1987 (Issued: 5,694)................... £1500	1988 (Issued: 3,315)............................. £1500

* Coins marked thus were originally issued in Royal Mint sets.
** Numbers include coins sold in sets

SE6

SE6   Five pounds 500th Anniversary of Sovereign. For the obverse impression a representation
Of Ourself as at Our Coronation, seated in King Edward's Chair and having received
the Sceptre with the Cross and the Rod with the Dove, all within the circumscription
'ELIZABETH.II.DEI.GRA.REG.FID.DEF' and for the reverse a Shield of Our Royal
Arms ensigned by an open Royal Crown, the whole superimposed upon a double Rose,
and with the circumscription 'ANNIVERSARY OF THE GOLD SOVEREIGN 1489-
1989' (Designs: Bernald Sindall)

1989 (Issued: 2,937)...£1800
—   Proof *FDC* (see PGS10)*...£2500

Obverse portrait by Ian Rank-Broadley

SE7

SE7   Five pounds. R. St.George

1998 Proof *FDC* (see PGS28)*... £1700	2004 Unc (Issued: 1,000)......................£1500
1999 Proof *FDC* (see PGS30)*... £1700	— Proof *FDC* (see PGS40)* £1700
2000 Bullion type........................ £1500	2006 Unc (Issued: 731)........................£1500
— Proof *FDC* (see PGS32)*.... £1700	— Proof *FDC* (see PGS44)* £1700
2001 Proof *FDC* (see PGS34)*... £1700	2007 Unc (Issued: 768)........................£1500
2003 Unc (Issued: 812).............. £1500	— Proof *FDC* (see PGS46)* £1700
— Proof *FDC* (see PGS38)*.... £1700	2008 Unc (Issued: 750)........................£1500
	— Proof *FDC* (see PGS49)* £1700

SE8   Five pounds. R. St. George, 'U' in a circle to left of date

1998 (Issued: 825) £1500	2000 (Issued: 994) £1500
1999 (Issued: 970) £1500	2001 (Issued: 1,000) £1500

* Coins marked thus were originally issued in Royal Mint sets.

SE9 SE10 SE11

SE9 **Five pounds.** R. The Shield of Arms of Our United Kingdom of Great Britain and Northern Ireland within an open wreath of laurel and ensigned by Our Royal Crown and beneath the date of the year. (Reverse design: Timothy Noad)

2002 Unc (Issued: 1,370)..£1650

— Proof *FDC* (see PGS36)*..£1800

SE10 **Five pounds.** R. A depiction of St George, carrying a shield and a sword, slaying the dragon, with the date '2005' beneath the wing of the dragon.(Reverse design: Timothy Noad)

2005 Unc (Issued: 936)...£1650

— Proof *FDC* (see PGS42)*..£1800

SE11 **Five pounds.** R. St George. Based on the original pattern piece of 1820 with the designer's name, 'PISTRUCCI', shown in full in the exergue, and with a broader rim.

2009 BU (Issued: 1,000)................£1550 — Proof *FDC* (see PGS52)*.................£1700

2010 BU (Issued: 1,000)................£1550 — Proof *FDC* (Edition: 2,000 in sets)* £1700

2011 BU (Issued: 657)...................£1550 — Proof *FDC* (Edition: 2,000 in sets)* £1700

2013 BU (Issued: 262)...................£1700 — Proof *FDC* (Issued: 388 in sets)*.....£1800

2014 BU (Edition 1,000)................£1550 — Proof *FDC* (Edition:) £1800

2015 Proof *FDC* (Edition: 600 including coins in sets)...£2000

SE12

SE12 Five pounds. R. The image of St George on horseback, attacking the dragon with a lance, with date of the year to the left. (Reverse design: Paul Day)

2012 BU (Issued: 496)..£2000

— Proof *FDC* (Issued: 956 coins in sets)* £2500

* Coins marked thus were originally issued in Royal Mint sets.

Obverse portrait by Jody Clark
SE13 Five pounds.
      2015 BU (Edition : 750)..£1600
      —   Proof *FDC* (Edition :600 including coins in sets)...............................£2500
      2016
      —   BU (Edition: 500)..£1725

Obverse portrait by James Butler

SE14
SE14 Five pounds. R. St George and Dragon.
      2016
      —   Proof *FDC* (Edition: 575 including coins in sets) £2500

Obverse portrait by Jody Clark

SE15

SE15 Five pounds R. The image of St George armed, sitting on horseback, attacking the
    dragon with a broken spear surrounded by the inscription 'HONI SOIT QUI MAL Y
    PENSE'.
    2017
    —   Proof *FDC* (Edition: 750 in sets)

* *Coins marked thus were originally issued in Royal Mint sets.*

In 1987 the Mint decided to enter the market for bullion coins and launched a series of four gold coins with weights that corresponded to those already issued by a number of gold producing countries such as Canada, South Africa and China. The plan was to sell bullion quality coins in quantity to trade customers and investors at modest premiums over the ruling gold market price, and also to sell proof versions in limited editions to collectors.

Due to market reaction, particularly from the Far East, silver rather than copper was alloyed with the gold in 1990 in an effort to increase demand but in the absence of sales figures, it appears that the major interest is now to be found among collectors of the proof collector versions.

To mark the 10th anniversary of the first design, silver coins struck in Britannia silver (0.958) were introduced in the same four weights. Again the main interest seems to have been among collectors of the proof versions although the one ounce silver bullion coin of £2 face value has proved popular as silver prices have risen.

There are some attractive and different interpretations of Britannia with the gold and silver issues sharing the same designs as they are changed. The range of designs thus far are shown below, and the complete sets are listed in the appropriate sections towards the end of the catalogue.

BRITANNIA SILVER

Obverse portrait by Ian Rank-Broadley

BA1

BA1　**Britannia. Five pence.** (1/40 oz of fine silver). R. A design of the standing figure of Britannia baring a trident and shield, with a lion at her feet, set against the backdrop of a globe, and with the inscription 'BRITANNIA 999 1/40 OZ FINE SILVER 2014' (Reverse design: Jody Clark)

　　2014 — Proof in silver *FDC* (0.999) (Edition: 2,750 including coins in sets)*
　　Illustration shown larger than actual coin diameter of 8mm

Obverse portrait by Jody Clark

BA2

BA2　**Britannia. Five pence.** (1/40 oz of fine silver). R. A figure of Britannia baring a trident and shield, set against a backdrop of a sailing ship, cliffs and a lighthouse with the inscription 'BRITANNIA 1/40 OZ FINE SILVER 999 2015' (Reverse design: Antony Dufort)

　　2015 — Proof in silver *FDC* (0.999) (Edition: 1,750 including coins in sets)*
　　Illustration shown larger than actual coin diameter of 8mm

* Coins marked thus were originally issued in Royal Mint sets.

BA3

BA3 **Britannia. Five pence.** (1/40 oz of fine silver). R. A standing figure of Britannia
holding in her left hand a trident and in her right hand a shield with a lion in the
background and the inscription 'BRITANNIA 1/40th OUNCE FINE SILVER 999
2016'. (Reverse design: Suzie Zamit)
2016 – Proof in silver *FDC* (0.999) (Edition: 1,100 including coins in sets)
Illustration shown larger than actual coin diameter of 8mm

Obverse portrait by Ian Rank-Broadley

BB1   BB2

BB1 **Britannia. Ten pence.** (1/20 oz of fine silver) (Previously listed as 4550) R. Seated
figure of Britannia holding a trident with a shield at her side and an owl upon her
knee with the word 'BRITANNIA' and the date of the year above and the inscription
'1/20 OUNCE FINE SILVER' below the figure of Britannia. (Reverse design:
Robert Hunt)
2013 — Proof in silver *FDC* (0.999) (Edition: 12,000 including coins in sets)*
BB2 **Britannia. Ten pence.** (1/20 oz of fine silver) R. A design of the standing figure
of Britannia baring a trident and shield, with a lion at her feet, set against the
backdrop of a globe, and with the inscription ' BRITANNIA 999 1/20 OZ FINE
SILVER 2014' (Reverse design: Jody Clark)
2014 — Proof in silver *FDC* (0.999) (Edition: 3,300 including coins in sets)*

Obverse portrait by Jody Clark

BB3   BB4

BB3 **Britannia. Ten pence.** (1/20 oz of fine silver) A figure of Britannia baring a trident
and shield, set against a backdrop of a sailing ship, cliffs and a lighthouse with the
inscription 'BRITANNIA 1/20 OZ FINE SILVER 999 2015' (Reverse design:
Antony Dufort)
2015 — Proof in silver *FDC* (0.999) (Edition: 3,300 including coins in sets)*
BB4 **Ten pence.** (1/20th oz. of fine silver). R. A standing figure of Britannia holding in
her left hand a trident and in her right hand a shield with a lion in the background
and the inscription 'BRITANNIA 1/20th OZ FINE SILVER 999 2016'. (Reverse
design: Suzie Zamit)
2016 – Proof in silver *FDC* – 0.999) (Edition: 1,100 including coins in sets)

* *Coins marked thus were originally issued in Royal Mint sets.*

Obverse portrait by Raphael Maklouf

BC1

BC1 **Britannia. Twenty pence.** (1/10 oz of fine silver) 10th Anniversary of Britannia
issue R. The figure of Britannia standing in a chariot drawn along the seashore by
two horses, with the word 'BRITANNIA', the inscription. 'TENTH OUNCE FINE
SILVER' and the date of the year. (Reverse design: Philip Nathan).
1997 Proof *FDC* (Issued: 8,686, plus coins issued in sets, see PSB01).........................£20

Obverse portrait by Ian Rank-Broadley

BC2   BC3   BC4

BC2 **Britannia. Twenty pence.** (1/10 oz of fine silver) R. The figure of Britannia standing
upon a rock in the sea, her right hand grasping a trident and her left hand resting on a
shield and holding an olive branch, with the word 'BRITANNIA', the date of the year,
and the inscription '1/10 OUNCE FINE SILVER'. (Reverse design: Philip Nathan).
(See 4500)
1998 — Proof *FDC* (Issued: 2,724, plus coins issued in sets, see PSB02)....................£20
2006 BU version...£15
2012 — Proof *FDC* (Issued: 2,595 in sets see PBS14)*

BC3 **Britannia. Twenty pence.** (1/10 oz of fine silver) R. The figure of Britannia, as
guardian, with a shield in her left hand and a trident in her right hand, accompanied by a
lion and, against the background of a wave motif, the words 'TENTH OUNCE FINE
SILVER' to the left and 'BRITANNIA' and the date of the year to the right. (Reverse
design: Philip Nathan).
2001 — Proof *FDC* (Issued: 826, plus coins issued in sets, see PSB03).......................£20

BC4 **Britannia. Twenty pence.** (1/10 oz fine silver) R. Helmeted head of Britannia with,
to the left, the word 'BRITANNIA' and, to the right, the inscription 'TENTH OUNCE
FINE SILVER' and the date of the year, the whole being overlaid with a wave pattern.
(Reverse design: Philip Nathan)
2003 — Proof *FDC* (Issued: 1,179, plus coins issued in sets, see PBS04)....................£20

BC5 **Britannia. Twenty pence.** (1/10 oz of fine silver) R. Seated figure of Britannia facing
to the left holding a trident with a shield at her side, with the word 'BRITANNIA', the
inscription 'TENTH OUNCE FINE SILVER' and the date of the year. (Reverse design:
Philip Nathan)
2005 — Proof *FDC** (Issued: 913, plus coins issued in sets, see PBS06)....................£20

* Coins marked thus were originally issued in Royal Mint sets.

BC6   BC8   BC9

BC6 **Britannia. Twenty pence.** (1/10 oz of fine silver) R. Seated figure of Britannia facing right holding a trident in her right hand and a sprig of olive in the left hand with a lion at her feet with the inscription 'TENTH OUNCE FINE SILVER' and the word 'BRITANNIA' and the date of the year (Reverse design: Christopher Le Brun)
2007 — Proof *FDC* (Issued: 901, plus coins issued in sets, see PBS08).......................£20

BC7 **Britannia. Twenty pence.** (1/10 oz of fine silver) R. A Standing figure of Britannia holding a trident with a shield at her side, the folds of her dress transforming into a wave, with the word 'BRITANNIA' and the date of the year and the inscription '1/10 OUNCE FINE SILVER' (Reverse design: John Bergdahl). (See 4506)
2008 — Proof *FDC* (Edition: 2,500, plus coins issued in sets, see PBS1010)..............£20

BC8 **Britannia. Twenty pence.** (1/10 oz fine silver) R. Standing figure of Britannia in horse drawn chariot. (See 4501)
2009 — Proof *FDC* (Edition; 3,500 including coins in sets)...£25

BC9 **Britannia. Twenty pence.** (1/10 oz fine silver) R. A design depicting a profile bust of Britannia wearing a helmet, accompanied by the name 'BRITANNIA', the inscription '1/10 OUNCE FINE SILVER' and the date '2010'. (Reverse design: Suzie Zamit)
2010 Proof *FDC* (Edition: 8,000 including coins in sets)..£25

BC10 **Britannia. Twenty pence.** (1/10 oz fine silver) R. A design depicting a seated figure of Britannia set against a background of a rippling Union Flag accompanied by the words '1/10 OUNCE FINE SILVER BRITANNIA' and the date '2011'. (Reverse design: David Mach)
2011 — Proof *FDC* (Edition: 6,000 including coins in sets)

BC11   BC12

BC11 **Britannia. Twenty pence.** (1/10 oz of fine silver).R. Seated figure of Britannia holding a trident with a shield at her side and an owl upon her knee with the word 'BRITANNIA' and the date of the year above and the inscription '1/10 OUNCE FINE SILVER' below the figure of Britannia. (Reverse design: Robert Hunt)
2013 — Proof in silver *FDC* (0.999) (Edition: 12,000 including coins in sets)*

BC12 **Britannia. Twenty pence.** (1/10 oz of fine silver) R. A design of the standing figure of Britannia baring a trident and shield, with a lion at her feet, set against the backdrop of a globe , and with the inscription ' BRITANNIA 999 1/10 OZ FINE SILVER 2014' (Reverse design: Jody Clark)
2014— Proof in silver *FDC* (0.999) (Edition: 3,300 including coins in sets)*

* Coins marked thus were originally issued in Royal Mint sets.

Obverse portrait by Jody Clark

BC13   BC14

BC13 Britannia. Twenty pence. (1/10 oz of fine silver) R. A figure of Britannia baring a trident and shield, set against a backdrop of a sailing ship, cliffs and a lighthouse with the inscription 'BRITANNIA 1/10 OZ FINE SILVER 999 2015' (Reverse design: Antony Dufort)

2015 – Proof in silver *FDC* (0.999) (Edition: 3,300 including coins in sets)*

BC14 Britannia. Twenty pence. (1/10th oz. of fine silver) R. A standing figure of Britannia holding in her left hand a trident and in her right hand a shield with a lion in the background and the inscription 'BRITANNIA 1/10TH OZ FINE SILVER 999 2016'. (Reverse design: Suzie Zamit)

2016 – Proof in silver *FDC* 0.999 (Edition: 1,100 including coins in sets)

Obverse portrait by Raphael Maklouf

BD1

BD1 Britannia. Fifty pence. (1/4 oz of fine silver) 10th Anniversary of Britannia issue R. The figure of Britannia standing in a chariot drawn along the seashore by two horses, with the word 'BRITANNIA', the inscription. 'QUARTER OUNCE FINE SILVER' and the date of the year. (Reverse design: Philip Nathan).

1997 Proof *FDC* (in 1997 sets, see PSB01)* £30

Obverse portrait by Ian Rank-Broadley

BD2

BD2 Britannia. Fifty pence. (1/4 oz of fine silver) R. The figure of Britannia standing upon a rock in the sea, her right hand grasping a trident and her left hand resting on a shield and holding an olive branch, the word 'BRITANNIA', the date of the year, and the inscription '1/4 OUNCE FINE SILVER'. (Reverse design: Philip Nathan).

1998 — Proof *FDC* (in 1998 set, see PSB02)* £25

2012 — Proof *FDC* (Issued: 2,595 in sets see PBS14)*

* Coins marked thus were originally issued in Royal Mint sets.

BD2A Britannia. Fifty pence. (1/4 oz of fine silver, 0.999 fine) R. The figure of Britannia
standing upon a rock in the sea, her .right hand grasping a trident and her left hand resting
on a shield and holding an olive branch, with the word 'BRITANNIA', the date of the year,
and the inscription' ¼ OUNCE FINE SILVER'. With the edge inscription 'SS Gairsoppa'
(Reverse design: Philip Nathan)
2013
2014 (Edition: 20,000) £20

4520B

BD2B Britannia. Fifty pence. (1/4 oz of fine silver). R. The figure of Britannia standing upon
a rock in the sea, her right hand grasping a trident and her left hand resting on a shield
and holding an olive branch, with the word 'BRITANNIA', the date of the year, and the
inscription' 1/4 OUNCE 999 FINE SILVER' and textured background on the obverse and
reverse. (Reverse design: Philip Nathan)
2015 – Bullion

BD3

BD3   Britannia. Fifty pence. (1/4 oz of fine silver) R. The figure of Britannia, as guardian, with a
shield in her left hand and a trident in her right hand, accompanied by a lion and, against the
background of a wave motif, the words 'QUARTER OUNCE FINE SILVER' to the left and
'BRITANNIA' and the date of the year to the right. . (Reverse design: Philip Nathan).
2001 — Proof *FDC* (in 2001 set, see PSB03)* £25

BD4

BD4   Britannia. Fifty pence. (1/4 oz fine silver) R. Helmeted head of Britannia with, to the left, the
word 'BRITANNIA' and, to the right, the inscription 'QUARTER OUNCE FINE SILVER' and
the date of the year, the whole being overlaid with a wave pattern. (Reverse design:
Philip Nathan)
2003 — Proof *FDC** £25

BD5   Britannia. Fifty pence. (Previously listed as 4514) (1/4 oz of fine silver) R. Seated figure
of Britannia facing to the left holding a trident with a shield at her side, with the word
'BRITANNIA', the inscription '1/4 OUNCE FINE SILVER' and the date of the year.
(Reverse design: Philip Nathan). (See 4504)
2005 — Proof *FDC** £25

* Coins marked thus were originally issued in Royal Mint sets.

BD6   BD7

BD6 **Britannia. Fifty pence.** (1/4 oz of fine silver) R. Seated figure of Britannia facing right holding a trident in her right hand and a sprig of olive in the left hand with a lion at her feet with the inscription 'QUARTER OUNCE FINE SILVER' and the word 'BRITANNIA' and the date of the year. (Reverse design: Christopher Le Brun)
2007 — Proof *FDC**...£25

BD7 **Britannia. Fifty pence.** (1/4 oz of fine silver) R. A Standing figure of Britannia holding a trident with a shield at her side, the folds of her dress transforming into a wave, with the word 'BRITANNIA' and the date of the year and the inscription '1/4 OUNCE FINE SILVER' (Reverse design: John Bergdahl)
2008 — Proof *FDC**...£25

BD8 **Britannia. Fifty pence.** (1/4 oz fine silver) R. Standing figure of Britannia in horse drawn chariot. (see 4300B above)
2009 — Proof *FDC**...£30

BD9   BD11

BD9 **Britannia. Fifty pence.** (1/4 oz fine silver) R. A design depicting a profile bust of Britannia wearing a helmet, accompanied by the name 'BRITANNIA', the inscription '1/4 OUNCE FINE SILVER' and the date '2010'. (Reverse design: Suzie Zamit)
2010 Proof *FDC* *..£30

BD10 **Britannia. Fifty pence.** (1/4 oz fine silver) R. A design depicting a seated figure of Britannia set against a background of a rippling Union Flag accompanied by the words '1/4 OUNCE FINE SILVER BRITANNIA' and the date '2011'. (Reverse design: David Mach)
2011 Proof *FDC* (Edition: 5,000 including coins in sets)..£30

BD11 **Britannia. Fifty pence.** (1/4 oz of fine silver).R. . Seated figure of Britannia holding a trident with a shield at her side and an owl upon her knee with the word 'BRITANNIA' and the date of the year above and the inscription '1/4 OUNCE FINE SILVER' below the figure of Britannia. (Reverse design: Robert Hunt)
2013 — Proof in silver *FDC* (0.999) (Issued: 3,087 including coins in sets)*

* *Coins marked thus were originally issued in Royal Mint sets.*

BD12

BD12 Britannia. Fifty pence. (Previously listed as 4530). (1/4 oz of fine silver) R. A design of the standing figure of Britannia baring a trident and shield, with a lion at her feet, set against the backdrop of a globe, and with the inscription 'BRITANNIA 999 1/4 OZ FINE SILVER 2014' (Reverse design: Jody Clark)
2014 — Proof in silver *FDC* (0.999) (Edition: 2,300 including coins in sets)*

Obverse portrait by Jody Clark

BD13   BD14

BD13 Britannia. Fifty pence. (1/4 oz of fine silver) R. A figure of Britannia baring a trident ... and shield, set against a backdrop of a sailing ship, cliffs and a lighthouse with the inscription 'BRITANNIA 1/4 OZ FINE SILVER 999 2015' (Reverse design: Antony Dufort)
2015 – Proof in silver *FDC* (0.999) (Edition: 2,300 including coins in sets)*

BD14 Britannia. Fifty pence. (1/4 oz. of fine silver) R. A standing figure of Britannia holding in her left hand a trident and in her right hand a shield with a lion in the background and the inscription 'BRITANNIA 1/4 OZ FINE SILVER 999 2016'. (Reverse design: Suzie Zamit)
2016 – Proof in silver *FDC* – 0.999 (Edition: 1,110 including coins in sets)

Obverse portrait by Raphael Maklouf

BE1

BE1   Britannia. One pound. (1/2 oz of fine silver) 10th Anniversary of Britannia issue. R. The figure of Britannia standing in a chariot drawn along the seashore by two horses, with the word 'BRITANNIA', the inscription. 'HALF OUNCE FINE SILVER' and the date of the year. (Reverse design: Philip Nathan).
1997 Proof *FDC*..£40

* Coins marked thus were originally issued in Royal Mint sets.

Obverse portrait by Ian Rank-Broadley

BE2   BE3

BE2 **Britannia. One pound.** (1/2 oz of fine silver) ℞. The figure of Britannia standing upon a
rock in the sea, her right hand grasping a trident and her left hand resting on a shield and
holding an olive branch, with the word 'BRITANNIA', the date of the year, and the
inscription '1/2 OUNCE FINE SILVER' (Reverse design: Philip Nathan).
1998 — Proof *FDC**...£40
2012 — Proof *FDC* (Issued: 4,251 in sets see PBS14 and PBS15)*

BE2A 2007 Proof with satin finish on reverse (see 2007 set, PBS09) *.......................................£40

BE3 **Britannia. One pound.** (1/2oz of fine silver) ℞ The figure of Britannia, as guardian,
with a shield in her left hand and a trident in her right hand, accompanied by a lion
and, against the background of a wave motif, the words 'HALF OUNCE FINE SILVER'
to the left and 'BRITANNIA' and the date of the year to the right. (Reverse design:
Philip Nathan).
2001 — Proof *FDC**...£40
2012 — Proof *FDC* (Issued: 1,656 in sets see PBS15)*

BE3A 2007 Proof with satin finish on reverse (see 2007 set, PBS09) *.......................................£40

BE4

BE4 **Britannia. One pound.** (1/2 oz fine silver) ℞. Helmeted head of Britannia with, to the
left, the word 'BRITANNIA' and, to the right, the inscription 'HALF OUNCE FINE
SILVER' and the date of the year, the whole being overlaid with a wave pattern.
(Reverse design: Philip Nathan)
2003 — Proof *FDC**...£40
2012 — Proof *FDC* (Issued: 1,656 in sets see PBS15)*

BE4A 2007 Proof with satin finish on reverse (see 2007 set, PBS09) *.......................................£40

BE5 **Britannia. One pound.** (1/2 oz of fine silver) ℞. Seated figure of Britannia facing to
the left holding a trident with a shield at her side, with the word 'BRITANNIA', the
inscription '1/2 OUNCE FINE SILVER' and the date of the year. (Reverse design:
Philip Nathan).
2005 — Proof *FDC**...£40
2012 — Proof *FDC* (Issued: 1,656 in sets see PBS15)*

BE5A 2007 Proof with satin finish on reverse (see 2007 set, PBS09) *.......................................£40

* *Coins marked thus were originally issued in Royal Mint sets.*

4514   4516

BE6 **Britannia. One pound.** (1/2 oz of fine silver) Ʀ. Seated figure of Britannia facing
right holding a trident in her right hand and a sprig of olive in the left hand with a lion
at her feet with the inscription 'HALF OUNCE FINE SILVER' and the word
'BRITANNIA' and the date of the year. (Reverse design: Christopher Le Brun)
2007 Proof *FDC* * £40
2012 — Proof *FDC* (Issued: 1,656 in sets see PBS15)*

BE6A 2007 Proof with satin finish on reverse (see 2007 set, PBS09) * £40

BE7 **Britannia. One pound.** (1/2 oz of fine silver) Ʀ. Standing figure of Britannia in
horse drawn chariot.
2007 Proof with satin finish on reverse (see 2007 set, PBS09) * £40

BE8 **Britannia. One pound.** (1/2 oz of fine silver) Ʀ. A Standing figure of Britannia holding
a trident with a shield at her side, the folds of her dress transforming into a wave, with
the word 'BRITANNIA' and the date of the year and the inscription '1/2 OUNCE FINE
SILVER' (Reverse design: John Bergdahl)
2008 Proof *FDC* * £40
2012 — Proof *FDC* (Issued: 1,656 in sets see PBS15)*

BE9   BE10   BE11

BE9 **Britannia. One pound.** (1/2 oz fine silver) Ʀ. Standing figure of Britannia in horse
drawn chariot. (Reverse design: Philip Nathan)
2009 — Proof *FDC** £40
2012 — Proof *FDC* (Issued: 1,656 in sets see PBS15)*

BE10 **Britannia. One pound.** (1/2 oz fine silver) Ʀ. A design depicting a profile bust of
Britannia wearing a helmet, accompanied by the name 'BRITANNIA', the inscription
'1/2 OUNCE FINE SILVER' and the date '2010'. (Reverse design: Suzie Zamit)
2010 Proof *FDC* * £40
2012 — Proof *FDC* (Issued: 1,656 in sets see PBS15)*

BE11 **Britannia. One pound.** (1/2 oz fine silver) Ʀ. A design depicting a seated figure of
Britannia set against a background of a rippling Union Flag accompanied by the words
'1/2 OUNCE FINE SILVER BRITANNIA' and the date '2011'. (Reverse design:
David Mach)
2011 Proof *FDC* (Edition: 5,000 including coins in sets) £40
2012 — Proof *FDC* (Issued: 1,656 in sets see PBS15)*

* Coins marked thus were originally issued in Royal Mint sets.

BE12   BE13

BE12 Britannia. One pound. (1/2 oz of fine silver) R. Seated figure of Britannia holding
a trident with a shield at her side and an owl upon her knee with the word
'BRITANNIA' and the date of the year above and the inscription '1/2 OUNCE FINE
SILVER' below the figure of Britannia. (Reverse design: Robert Hunt)
2013 — Proof in silver *FDC* (0.999) (Issued: 3,087 including coins in sets)*

BE13 Britannia. One pound. (1/2 oz of fine silver) R. A design of the standing figure of
Britannia baring a trident and shield, with a lion at her feet, set against the backdrop
of a globe , and with the inscription ' BRITANNIA 999 1/2 OZ FINE SILVER 2014'
(Reverse design: Jody Clark)
2014 — Proof in silver *FDC* (0.999) (Edition: 2,300 including coins in sets)*

Obverse portrait by Jody Clark

BE14

BE14 Britannia. One pound. (1/2 oz of fine silver) R. A figure of Britannia baring a trident
and shield, set against a backdrop of a sailing ship, cliffs and a lighthouse with the
inscription 'BRITANNIA 1/2 OZ FINE SILVER 999 2015' (Reverse design:
Antony Dufort)
2015 — Proof in silver *FDC* (0.999) (Edition: 2,300 including coins in sets)*

BE15

BE15 Britannia. One pound. (1/2 oz. of fine silver). R. A standing figure of Britannia holding
in her left hand a trident and in her right hand a shield with a lion in the background and
the inscription 'BRITANNIA 1/2 OZ FINE SILVER 999 2016'. (Reverse design:
Suzie Zamit)
2016 – Proof in silver *FDC* – 0.999 (Edition: 1,110 including coins in sets)

* Coins marked thus were originally issued in Royal Mint sets.

Obverse portrait by Raphael Maklouf

BF1

BF1　Britannia. Two pounds. (1 oz fine silver) 10th Anniversary of Britannia issue R. The figure of Britannia standing in a chariot drawn along the seashore by two horses, with the word 'BRITANNIA', the inscription. 'ONE OUNCE FINE SILVER' and the date of the year. (Reverse design: Philip Nathan)
　　　1997 Proof *FDC* (Issued: 4,173)...£120

Obverse portrait by Ian Rank-Broadley

BF2

BF2　Britannia. Two pounds. (1 oz of fine silver) R. The figure of Britannia standing upon a rock in the sea, her right hand grasping a trident and her left hand resting on a shield and holding an olive branch, with the word 'BRITANNIA', the date of the year, and the inscription' ONE OUNCE FINE SILVER'. (Reverse design: Philip Nathan)

1998 (Issued: 88,909).....................£40	2006 (Edition 100,000)..............................£40
—　Proof *FDC* (Issued: 2,168)......£80	—　Proof *FDC* (Issued: 2,529)................£65
2000 (Issued: 81,301).....................£40	2012 (Edition 100,000).............................£58
2002 (Issued: 36,543).....................£40	— Proof *FDC* (Issued 5,532 including coins
2004 (Edition: 100,000)　　　　 £40	in sets) £93
—　Proof *FDC* (Issued: 2,174)......£65	

BF2A Britannia. Two pounds. (1 oz of fine silver) R. Standing figure of Britannia
　　　2006 – Proof *FDC** with selected gold plating of obverse and reverse (See PBS07)......£70
BF2B Britannia. Two pounds. (1 oz. of fine silver – 0.999)
　　　2013 (Issued: 2,387)

* Coins marked thus were originally issued in Royal Mint sets.

BF2C Britannia. Two pounds. (1 oz. of fine silver – 0.999) R. With revised inscription 'BRITANNIA 2014 1 oz. 999 FINE SILVER'

2014

— (Edition: 10,000) £58

2015 As 2014 but dated 2015

— (Edition: 10,000) £58

BF2D Britannia. Two pounds. (Previously listed as 4500B). (1 oz. of fine silver – 0.999)

2013

— As above but with edge decoration of snake design symbolising the Year of the Snake.

BF2E Britannia. Two pounds. (1 oz. of fine silver – 0.999)

2014

— As above but with edge decoration of horse design symbolising Year of the Horse

BF2F Two pounds. Error obverse – known as a Mule. The obverse design of The Queen used for the Year of the Horse £2 Silver coin was paired with the reverse design of the Britannia £2 silver coin.

2014

BF3

BF3 Britannia. Two pounds. (1 oz. of fine silver – 0.999). R. As 4500 above but with revised inscription 'BRITANNIA 2015 1 OZ 999 FINE SILVER' (Reverse design: Philip Nathan).

2015 — BU

BF4

BF4 Britannia. Two pounds. (1 oz. of fine silver – 0.999). R. As 4500 above but with revised inscription 'BRITANNIA 2015 1 OZ 999 FINE SILVER' and textured background on the obverse and reverse. (Reverse design: Philip Nathan).

2015 — Bullion

* Coins marked thus were originally issued in Royal Mint sets.

Obverse portrait by Jody Clark

BF5

BF5   Britannia. Two pounds. (1 oz. of fine silver – 0.999). R. As 4500 above but with revised inscription 'BRITANNIA 2016 1OZ 999 FINE SILVER' (Reverse design: Philip Nathan). 2016 — BU

BF6

BF6   Britannia. Two pounds. (1 oz. of fine silver – 0.999) R. As 4500 above but with revised inscription 'BRITANNIA 2016 1 OZ 999 FINE SILVER' and textured background on the obverse and reverse. (Reverse design: Philip Nathan). 2016 — Bullion

BF7

BF7   Britannia. Two pounds. (1oz fine silver) R. Standing figure of Britannia in horse drawn chariot.(Reverse design: Philip Nathan)

1999 (Issued: 69,394)..£40
2009 (Issued: 100,000)..£40
—   Proof *FDC* (Edition: 12,000 including coins in sets)...£65

BF7A Britannia. Two pounds. (1 oz of fine silver) R. Standing figure of Britannia in horse drawn chariot

2006 — Proof *FDC** with selected gold plating of obverse and reverse (See PBS07)....£70

BF8 BF9

BF8 **Britannia. Two pounds.** (1 oz of fine silver) R. The figure of Britannia, as guardian, with a shield in her left hand and a trident in her right hand, accompanied by a lion and, against the background of a wave motif, the words 'ONE OUNCE FINE SILVER' to the left and 'BRITANNIA' and the date of the year to the right. (Reverse design: Philip Nathan)
2001 (Issued: 44,816)..£40
— Proof *FDC* (Issued: 3,047)..£60

BF8A **Britannia. Two pounds.** (1 oz of fine silver) R. Helmeted figure of Britannia holding a trident and a shield with a lion in the background
2006 — Proof *FDC** with selected gold plating of obverse and reverse (See PBS07)....£70

BF9 **Britannia. Two pounds.** (1oz fine silver) R. Helmeted head of Britannia with, to the left, the word 'BRITANNIA' and, to the right, the inscription 'ONE OUNCE FINE SILVER' and the date of the year, the whole being overlaid with a wave pattern. (Reverse design: Philip Nathan)
2003 (Issued: 73,271)..£40
— Proof *FDC* (Issued: 2,016)..£65

BF9A **Britannia. Two pounds.** (1oz fine silver) R. Helmeted figure of Britannia with stylised waves
2006 — Proof *FDC** with selected gold plating of obverse and reverse (See PBS07)....£70

BF10

BF10 **Britannia. Two pounds.** (1 oz of fine silver) R. Seated figure of Britannia facing to the left holding a trident with a shield at her side, with the word 'BRITANNIA', the inscription 'ONE OUNCE FINE SILVER' and the date of the year. (Reverse design: Philip Nathan)
2005 (Edition: 100,000) £40
— Proof *FDC* (Issued: 1,539)..£65

BF10A **Britannia. Two pounds.** (1 oz of fine silver) R. Seated figure of Britannia facing left
2006 — Proof *FDC** with selected gold plating of obverse and reverse (See PBS07)....£70

* *Coins marked thus were originally issued in Royal Mint sets.*

BF11   BF12

BF11 Britannia. Two pounds. (1 oz of fine silver) R. Seated figure of Britannia facing right
holding a trident in her right hand and a sprig of olive in the left hand with a lion at her feet
with the inscription 'ONE OUNCE FINE SILVER' and the word 'BRITANNIA' and the
date of the year. (Reverse design: Christopher Le Brun)
2007 (Edition: 100,000) £40
—   Proof *FDC* (Issued: 5,157)...£65

BF12 Britannia. Two pounds. (1 oz of fine silver) R. A Standing figure of Britannia holding a
trident with a shield at her side, the folds of her dress transforming into a wave, with the word
'BRITANNIA' and the date of the year and the inscription 'ONE OUNCE FINE SILVER'
(Reverse design: John Bergdahl)
2008 (Edition: 100,000) £40
—   Proof *FDC* (Edition: 2,500) £65

BF13   BF14

BF13 Britannia. Two pounds. (1 oz fine silver) R. A design depicting a profile bust of
Britannia wearing a helmet, accompanied by the name 'BRITANNIA', the inscription
'ONE OUNCE FINE SILVER' and the date '2010'. (Reverse design: Suzie Zamit)
2010 (Edition: 100,000) £40
—   Proof *FDC* (Edition: 8,000 including coins in sets)..£65

BF14 Britannia. Two pounds. (1 oz fine silver) R. A design depicting a seated figure of
Britannia set against a background of a rippling Union Flag accompanied by the words
'ONE OUNCE FINE SILVER BRITANNIA' and the date '2011'.
(Reverse design: David Mach)
2011 (Edition: 500,000)...£58
—   Proof *FDC* (Edition: 10,000) £90

* Coins marked thus were originally issued in Royal Mint sets.

BF15

BF15 Britannia. Two pounds. (1 oz of fine silver) R. Seated figure of Britannia holding a
trident with a shield at her side and an owl upon her knee with the word 'BRITANNIA'
and the date of the year above and the inscription 'ONE OUNCE FINE SILVER' below
the figure of Britannia. (Reverse design: Robert Hunt)
2013 — Proof in silver *FDC* (0.999) (Issued: 7,555 including coins in sets)................£93

BF16

BF16 Britannia. Two pounds. (Previously listed as 4540). (1 oz of fine silver) R. A design
of the standing figure of Britannia baring a trident and shield, with a lion at her feet,
set against the backdrop of a globe, and with the inscription 'BRITANNIA 999 1 OZ
FINE SILVER 2014' (Reverse design: Jody Clark)
2014 — Proof in silver *FDC* (0.999) (Edition: 5,300 including coins in sets) £83

* Coins marked thus were originally issued in Royal Mint sets.

Obverse portrait by Jody Clark

BF17

BF17 Britannia. Two pounds. (1 oz of fine silver) R. A figure of Britannia baring a
trident and shield, set against a backdrop of a sailing ship, cliffs and a lighthouse
with the inscription 'BRITANNIA 1 OZ FINE SILVER 999 2015'
(Reverse design: Antony Dufort)
2015 — Proof in silver *FDC* (0.999) (Edition: 6,550 including coins in sets) £83

BF18

BF18 Britannia. Two pounds. (1 oz. of fine silver) R. A standing figure of Britannia holding
in her left hand a trident and in her right hand a shield with a lion in the background
and the inscription 'BRITANNIA 1 OZ FINE SILVER 999 2016'. (Reverse design:
Suzie Zamit)
2016 – Proof in silver *FDC* (0.999) (Edition: 7,000 including coins in sets)...................£83

Obverse portrait by Ian Rank-Broadley

BG1

BG1 Britannia. Ten pounds. (5 oz of fine silver). R. Seated figure of Britannia holding a
trident with a shield at her side and an owl upon her knee with the word 'BRITANNIA'
and the date of the year above and the inscription '5 OUNCES FINE SILVER'
below the figure of Britannia. (Reverse design: Robert Hunt)
2013 — Proof in silver FDC (0.999) (Issued: 4,054) £450
Illustration shown at a reduced size - actual coin diameter 63mm

BG2

BG2 Britannia. Ten pounds. (5 oz. of fine silver) R. A design of the standing figure of
Britannia baring a trident and shield, with a lion at her feet, set against the backdrop
of a globe, and with the inscription 'BRITANNIA 999 5 OZ FINE SILVER 2014'
(Reverse design: Jody Clark)
2014 — Proof in silver *FDC* (0.999) (Edition: 1,350) £395
Illustration shown at a reduced size - actual coin diameter 63mm

Obverse portrait by Jody Clark

BG3

BG3 Britannia. Ten pounds. (5 oz. of fine silver). R. A figure of Britannia baring a trident and
    shield, set against a backdrop of a sailing ship, cliffs and a lighthouse with the inscription
    'BRITANNIA 5 OZ FINE SILVER 999 2015' (Reverse design: Antony Dufort)
    2015 — Proof in silver *FDC* (0.999) (Edition: 1,150)...£395
    Illustration shown at reduced size – actual coin diameter 63mm

BG4

BG4   **Britannia. Ten pounds.** (5 oz. of fine silver) R. A standing figure of Britannia holding in
      her left hand a trident and in her right hand a shield with a lion in the background
      and the inscription 'BRITANNIA 5 OZ FINE SILVER 999 2016'. (Reverse design:
      Suzie Zamit)
      2016 — Proof in silver *FDC* (0.999) (Edition: 550) £395
      Illustration shown at reduced size – actual coin diameter 63mm

Obverse portrait by Ian Rank-Broadley

BH1 Britannia. Fifty pounds. (1 kilo of fine silver). R. A design of the figure of Britannia on a textured background standing upon a rock in the sea, her right hand grasping a trident and her left hand on a shield and holding an olive branch, with the inscription 'BRITANNIA' (and the date of the year) 1 KILO OF 999 FINE SILVER' (Original reverse design: Philip Nathan)
2014

Obverse portrait by Jody Clark

BH2

BH2 Britannia Fifty pounds. (1 oz fine silver - 0.999). R. A design of the standing figure of Britannia bearing a trident and a shield, with a lion at her feet, set against the backdrop of a globe, and the inscription 'BRITANNIA 50 POUNDS' and the date '2015' below. (Reverse design: Jody Clark).
2015 — Silver BU (Edition: 100,000)..£50

Obverse portrait by Ian Rank-Broadley

BJ1

BJ1   **Britannia. 50 pence.** (1/40 oz. of fine gold) R. A design of the standing figure of Britannia baring a trident and shield, with a lion at her feet, set against the backdrop of a globe, and with the inscription 'BRITANNIA 999.9 1/40 OZ FINE GOLD 2014'
(Reverse design: Jody Clark)
2014 — Proof in gold *FDC* (0.9999) (Edition: 10,000 including coins in sets)*............£50
Illustration shown larger than actual coin diameter of 8mm

Obverse portrait by Jody Clark

BJ2   BJ3

BJ2   **Britannia. 50 pence.** (1/40 oz. of fine gold)..R. A figure of Britannia baring a trident and shield, set against a backdrop of a sailing ship, cliffs and a lighthouse with the inscription 'BRITANNIA 999.9 1/40 OZ FINE GOLD 2015' (Reverse design: Antony Dufort)
2015 — Proof in gold *FDC* (0.9999) (Edition: 8,000 including coins in sets)*...............£50
Illustration shown larger than actual coin diameter of 8mm

BJ3   **Britannia. Fifty pence.** (1/40th oz. of fine gold) R. A standing figure of Britannia holding in her left hand a trident and in her right hand a shield with a lion in the background and the inscription 'BRITANNIA 1/40 OZ OUNCE FINE GOLD 2016'. (Reverse design: Suzie Zamit)
2016 — Proof in gold *FDC* (0.9999) (Edition:2,525 including coins in sets)..................£50
Illustration shown larger than actual coin diameter of 8mm

Obverse portrait by Ian Rank-Broadley

BL1   BL2

BL1   **Britannia. One pound.** (1/20 oz of fine gold) R. Seated figure of Britannia holding a trident with a shield at her side and an owl upon her knee with the word 'BRITANNIA' and the date of the year above and the inscription '1/20 OUNCE FINE GOLD' below the figure of Britannia. (Reverse design: Robert Hunt)
2013 — Proof in gold *FDC* (0.9999) (Issued: 2,496 including coins in sets) £100

BL2   **Britannia. One pound.** (1/20 oz of fine gold) R. A design of the standing figure of Britannia baring a trident and shield, with a lion at her feet, set against the backdrop of a globe , and with the inscription ' BRITANNIA 999.9 1/20 OZ FINE GOLD 2014'
(Reverse design: Jody Clark)
2014 — Proof in gold *FDC* (0.9999) (Edition: 1,550 including coins in sets)*..........£100

* Coins marked thus were originally issued in Royal Mint sets.
NB. The spot price of gold at the time of going to press was £1030 per oz.

Obverse portrait by Jody Clark

BL3   BL4

BL3 **Britannia. One pound.**(1/20 oz of fine gold)..R. A figure of Britannia baring a trident and shield, set against a backdrop of a sailing ship, cliffs and a lighthouse with the inscription 'BRITANNIA 1/20 OZ FINE GOLD 999.9 2015' (Reverse design: Antony Dufort)
2015 — Proof in gold *FDC* (0.9999) (Edition: 1,550 including coins in sets)*.............£100

BL4 **Britannia. One pound.** (1/20 oz. of fine gold) R. A standing figure of Britannia holding in her left hand a trident and in her right hand a shield with a lion in the background and the inscription 'BRITANNIA 1/20 OZ FINE GOLD 999.9 2016'. (Reverse design: Suzie Zamit)
2016 — Proof in gold *FDC* (0.9999) (Edition: 1,125 including coins in sets)..............£100

Obverse portrait by Raphael Maklouf

BM1   BM3

BM1 **Britannia. Ten pounds.** (1/10oz of fine gold alloyed with copper). R. The figure of Britannia standing upon a rock in the sea, her right hand grasping a trident and her left hand resting on a shield and holding an olive branch, with the inscription '1/10 OUNCE FINE GOLD BRITANNIA' and the year of the date. (Reverse design: Philip Nathan)

1987.. £130	1989 ....£130
— Proof *FDC* (Issued: 3,500).... £150	— Proof *FDC* (Issued: 1,609) £150
1988.. £130	
— Proof *FDC* (Issued: 2,694).... £150	

BM2 **Britannia. Ten pounds.** (1/10oz of fine gold alloyed with silver). R. Britannia standing.

1990.. £130	1994 ....£130
— Proof *FDC* (Issued: 1,571).... £150	— Proof *FDC* (Issued: 994) £150
1991.. £130	1995 ....£130
— Proof *FDC* (Issued: 954)....... £150	— Proof *FDC* (Issued: 1,500) £150
1992.. £130	1996 ....£130
— Proof *FDC* (Issued: 1,000).... £150	— Proof *FDC* (Issued: 2,379) £150
1993.. £130	
— Proof *FDC* (Issued: 997)....... £150	

BM3 **Britannia. Ten pounds.** (1/10 oz fine gold, alloyed with silver) 10th Anniversary of Britannia issue. R. The figure of Britannia standing in a chariot drawn along the seashore by two horses, with the word 'BRITANNIA', ... the inscription 'TENTH OUNCE FINE GOLD' and the date of the year. (Reverse design: Philip Nathan)
1997 Proof *FDC* (Issued: 1,821)...£180

* Coins marked thus were originally issued in Royal Mint sets.
NB. The spot price of gold at the time of going to press was £1030 per oz.

Obverse portrait by Ian Rank-Broadley

BM4

BM4 Britannia. Ten pounds. (1/10 oz fine gold alloyed with silver) ℞. The figure of Britannia
standing upon a rock in the sea, Her right hand grasping a trident and her left hand resting
on a shield and holding an olive branch, with the word 'BRITANNIA', the date of the year,
and the inscription '1/10 OUNCE FINE GOLD'. (Reverse design: Philip Nathan)

1998 Proof *FDC* (Issued: 392)...... £150	2002 Proof *FDC* (Issued: 1,500) £150
1999.. £130	2004 ....£130
1999 Proof *FDC* (Issued: 1,058)... £150	2004 Proof *FDC* (Issued: 929) £150
2000.. £130	2006 Proof *FDC* (issued: 700).................£150
2000 Proof *FDC* (Issued: 659)...... £150	2012 ....£150
2002.. £130	2012 Proof *FDC* (Issued: 1,249) £225

BM5   BM6   BM7   BM8

BM5 Britannia. Ten pounds. (1/10 oz fine gold alloyed with silver) ℞. The figure of Britannia, as
guardian, with a shield in her left hand and a trident in her right hand, accompanied by a lion
and, against the background of a wave motif, and the words 'TENTH OUNCE FINE GOLD' to
the left and 'BRITANNIA' and the date of the year to the right. (Reverse design: Philip Nathan)
2001.. £130   2001 Proof *FDC* (Issued: 1,557) £150

BM6 Britannia. Ten pounds. (1/10 oz fine gold alloyed with silver) ℞. . Helmeted head of Britannia
with, to the left, the word 'BRITANNIA' and, to the right, the inscription 'TENTH OUNCE
FINE GOLD' and the date of the year, the whole being overlaid with a wave pattern. (Reverse
design: Philip Nathan)
2003.. £130   2003 Proof *FDC* (Issued: 1,382) £150

BM7 Britannia. Ten pounds. (1/10 oz fine gold alloyed with silver) ℞. Seated figure of
Britannia facing to the left holding a trident with a shield at her side, with the word
'BRITANNIA', the inscription 'TENTH OUNCE FINE GOLD' and the date of the year.
(Reverse design: Philip Nathan)
2005 Proof *FDC* (issued: 1,225) £150

BM8 Britannia. Ten pounds. (1/10 oz fine gold alloyed with silver) ℞. Seated figure of
Britannia facing right holding a trident in her right hand and a sprig of olive in the left
hand with a lion at her feet with the inscription 'TENTH OUNCE FINE GOLD' and the
word 'BRITANNIA' and the date of the year. (Reverse design: Christopher Le Brun)
2007.. £130   2007 Proof *FDC* (Issued: 893) £150

BM8A(1/10 oz platinum)
2007 Proof *FDC* (Issued: 691)..£225

* Coins marked thus were originally issued in Royal Mint sets.
NB. The spot price of gold at the time of going to press was £1030 per oz.

BM9 BM10 BM11

BM9 Britannia. Ten pounds. (1/10 oz fine gold alloyed with silver) R. A Standing figure of Britannia holding a trident with a shield at her side, the folds of her dress transforming into a wave, with the word 'BRITANNIA' and the date of the year and the inscription '1/10 OUNCE FINE GOLD' (Reverse design: John Bergdahl)

2008 Proof *FDC* (Issued: 748 plus coins issued in sets, see PBS30) £150

BM9A ....(1/10 oz platinum)

2008 Proof *FDC* (Issued: 268 plus coins issued in sets, see PPBCS2) £225

BM10 Britannia. Ten pounds. (1/10 oz fine gold alloyed with silver) R. Standing figure of Britannia in horse drawn chariot.

2009.. £130   2009 Proof *FDC* (Edition: 750)...............£160

BM11 Britannia. Ten pounds. (1/10 oz fine gold alloyed with silver) R. A design depicting a profile bust of Britannia wearing a helmet, accompanied by the name 'BRITANNIA', the inscription '1/10 OUNCE FINE GOLD' and the date '2010'. (Reverse design: Suzie Zamit)

2010 Proof *FDC* (Edition: 3,000 including coins in sets)...£160

BM12 Britannia. Ten pounds. (1/10 oz fine gold alloyed with silver) R. A design depicting a seated figure of Britannia set against a background of a rippling Union Flag accompanied by the words '1/10 OUNCE FINE GOLD BRITANNIA, and the date '2011'. (Reverse design: David Mach)

2011 Proof *FDC* (Edition: 8,000 including coins in sets)... £225

BM13

BM13 Britannia. Ten pounds. (1/10 oz of fine gold) R. Seated figure of Britannia holding a trident with a shield at her side and an owl upon her knee with the word 'BRITANNIA' and the date of the year above and the inscription '1/10 OUNCE FINE GOLD' below the figure of Britannia. (Reverse design: Robert Hunt)

2013 — Proof in gold *FDC* (0.9999) (Issued: 1,150 including coins in sets)*

BM14

BM14 Britannia. Ten pounds. (1/10 oz of fine gold) R. A design of the standing figure of Britannia baring a trident and shield, with a lion at her feet, set against the backdrop of a globe, and with the inscription 'BRITANNIA 999.9 1/10 OZ FINE GOLD 2014' (Reverse design: Jody Clark)

2014 — Proof in gold *FDC* (0.9999) (Edition: 650 including coins in sets)*

* Coins marked thus were originally issued in Royal Mint sets.
NB. The spot price of gold at the time of going to press was £1030 per oz.

BM15

BM15 Britannia. Ten pounds. (1/10 oz of fine gold). R. Design with textured background on
the obverse and reverse, and with the inscription ' BRITANNIA 2015 1/10 OZ 999.9
FINE GOLD' (Reverse design: Philip Nathan)
2015 — Bullion

Obverse portrait by Jody Clark

BM16   BM17

BM16 Britannia. Ten pounds. (1/10 oz of fine gold). R. Nathan design with textured
background on the obverse and reverse , and with the inscription ' BRITANNIA 2016
1/10 OZ 999.9 FINE GOLD' (Reverse design: Philip Nathan)
2016 — Bullion

BM17 Britannia. Ten pounds. (1/10 oz. of fine gold – 0.9999) R. A standing figure of
Britannia holding in her left hand a trident and in her right hand a shield with a lion in the
background and the inscription 'BRITANNIA 1/10 OUNCE FINE GOLD 999.9 2016'.
(Reverse design: Suzie Zamit)
2016 — Proof in gold *FDC* (Edition: 1,125 including coins in sets)

Obverse portrait by Raphael Maklouf

BN1

BN1   Britannia. Twenty five pounds. (1/4oz of fine gold alloyed with copper). R. The figure
of Britannia standing upon a rock in the sea, her right hand grasping a trident and her left
hand resting on a shield and holding an olive branch, with the inscription '1/4 OUNCE
FINE GOLD BRITANNIA' and the year of the date. (Reverse design: Philip Nathan)

1987... £325	1989 ....£325
— Proof *FDC* (Issued: 3,500).... £350	— Proof *FDC* (see PBS05)* £350
1988... £325	
— Proof *FDC* (see PBS03)*...... £350	

* Coins marked thus were originally issued in Royal Mint sets.
NB. The spot price of gold at the time of going to press was £1030 per oz.

BN2 **Britannia. Twenty five pounds.** (1/4oz of fine gold alloyed with silver). R. Britannia standing.

1990	£325	1994	£325
— Proof *FDC* (see PBS07)*	£350	— Proof *FDC* (see PBS11)*	£350
1991	£325	1995	£325
— Proof *FDC* (see PBS08)*	£350	— Proof *FDC* (see PBS12)*	£350
1992	£325	1996	£325
— Proof *FDC* (see PBS09)*	£350	— Proof *FDC* (see PBS13	£350
1993	£325		
— Proof *FDC* (see PBS10)*	£350		

BN3

BN3 **Britannia. Twenty five pounds.** (1/4 oz fine gold, alloyed with silver) 10th Anniversary of Britannia issue. R. The figure of Britannia standing in a chariot drawn along the seashore by two horses, with the word 'BRITANNIA', the inscription. 'QUARTER OUNCE FINE GOLD' and the date of the year. (Reverse design: Philip Nathan)

1997 Proof *FDC* (Issued: 923).. £350

Obverse portrait by Ian Rank-Broadley

BN4   BN5

BN4 **Britannia. Twenty five pounds.** (1/4 oz fine gold alloyed with silver) R. The figure of Britannia standing upon a rock in the sea, her right hand grasping a trident and her left hand resting on a shield and holding an olive branch, with the word 'BRITANNIA', the date of the year, and the inscription' 1/4 OUNCE FINE GOLD'. (Reverse design: Philip Nathan)

1998 Proof *FDC* (Issued: 560)	£350	2002 Proof *FDC* (Issued: 750)	£350
1999	£325	2004 Proof *FDC* (Issued: 750)	£350
1999 Proof *FDC* (Issued: 1,000)	£350	2006 Proof *FDC* (Edition: 1,000)	£350
2000	£325	2012 Proof *FDC* (Issued: 316)	£500
2000 Proof *FDC* (Issued: 500)	£350		

BN5 **Britannia. Twenty five pounds.** (1/4 oz fine gold alloyed with silver) R. The figure of Britannia, as guardian, with a shield in her left hand and a trident in her right hand, accompanied by a lion and, against the background of a wave motif, the words 'QUARTER OUNCE FINE GOLD' to the left and 'BRITANNIA' and the date of the year to the right. (Reverse design: Philip Nathan)

2001	£325	2006 Proof *FDC* (see PBS28)*	£350
2001 Proof *FDC* (Issued: 500)	£350		

* Coins marked thus were originally issued in Royal Mint sets.
NB. The spot price of gold at the time of going to press was £1030 per oz

BN6   BN9

BN6 Britannia. Twenty five pounds. (1/4 oz fine gold alloyed with silver) R. Helmeted head of Britannia with, to the left, the word 'BRITANNIA' and, to the right, the inscription 'QUARTER OUNCE FINE GOLD' and the date of the year, the whole being overlaid with a wave pattern. (Reverse design: Philip Nathan)

    2003 Proof *FDC* (Issued: 609)...... £325   2006 Proof *FDC* (see PBS28)* £350

BN7 Britannia. Twenty five pounds. (1/4 oz fine gold alloyed with silver) R. Seated figure of Britannia facing to the left holding a trident with a shield at her side, with the word 'BRITANNIA', the inscription '1/4 OUNCE FINE GOLD' and the date of the year. (Reverse design: Philip Nathan)

    2005 Proof *FDC* (Issued: 750).....£325   2006 Proof *FDC* (seePBS28)* £350

BN8 Britannia. Twenty five pounds. (1/4 oz fine gold alloyed with silver) R. Standing figure of Britannia in horse drawn chariot. (See 4293)

    2006 Proof *FDC* (see PBS28)* ....£325   2009 Proof *FDC* (Edition: 1,000) £350

BN9 Britannia. Twenty five pounds. (Previously listed as 4474) (1/4 oz fine gold alloyed with silver) R. Seated figure of Britannia facing right holding a trident in her right hand and a sprig of olive in the left hand with a lion at her feet with the inscription 'QUARTER OUNCE FINE GOLD' and the word 'BRITANNIA' and the date of the year. (Reverse design: Christopher Le Brun)

    2007..£325   2007 Proof *FDC* (Issued: 1,000)............£350

BN9A (1/4 oz platinum)

    2007 Proof *FDC* (Issued: 210)..£450

BN9   BN10

BN10 Britannia. Twenty five pounds. (1/4 oz fine gold alloyed with silver) R. A Standing figure of Britannia holding a trident with a shield at her side, the folds of her dress transforming into a wave, with the word 'BRITANNIA' and the date of the year and the inscription '1/4 OUNCE FINE GOLD' (Reverse design: John Bergdahl)

    2008 Proof *FDC* (Edition: 1,000) £350

BN10A(1/4 oz platinum)

    2008 Proof *FDC* (Edition: 500) £450

BN11 Britannia. Twenty five pounds. (1/4 oz fine gold alloyed with silver) R. A design depicting a profile bust of Britannia wearing a helmet, accompanied by the name 'BRITANNIA', the inscription '1/4 OUNCE FINE GOLD' and the date '2010'. (Reverse design: Suzie Zamit)

    2010 Proof *FDC* (Edition: 3,000 including coins in sets)...£350

* Coins marked thus were originally issued in Royal Mint sets.
NB. The spot price of gold at the time of going to press was £1030 per oz.

BN12

BN12 Britannia. Twenty Five pounds. (1/4 oz fine gold alloyed with silver) R. A design depicting a seated figure of Britannia set against a background of a rippling Union Flag accompanied by the words ' 1/4 OUNCE FINE GOLD BRITANNIA, and the date '2011'. (Reverse design: David Mach)

2011 Proof *FDC* (Edition: 7,000 including coins in sets) £500

BN13 Britannia. Twenty five pounds. (1/4 oz of fine gold) R. Seated figure of Britannia holding a trident with a shield at her side and an owl upon her knee with the word 'BRITANNIA' and the date of the year above and the inscription '1/4 OUNCE FINE GOLD' below the figure of Britannia. (Reverse design: Robert Hunt)

2013 — Proof in gold *FDC* (0.9999) (Edition: 875 including coins in sets)*

BN14

BN14 Britannia. Twenty five pounds. (1/4 oz. of fine gold). R. Design with textured background on the obverse and reverse, and with the inscription ' BRITANNIA 2015 1/4 OZ 999.9 FINE GOLD' (Reverse design: Philip Nathan)

2015 — Bullion

Obverse portrait by Jody Clark

BN15

BN15 Britannia. Twenty five pounds. (1/4 oz of fine gold). R. A figure of Britannia baring a trident and shield, set against a backdrop of a sailing ship, cliffs and a lighthouse with the inscription 'BRITANNIA 1/4 OZ FINE GOLD 999.9 2015' (Reverse design: Antony Dufort) ....

2015 — Proof in gold *FDC* (0.9999) (Edition: 450 including coins in sets)*

* Coins marked thus were originally issued in Royal Mint sets.
NB. The spot price of gold at the time of going to press was £1030 per oz.

BN16

BN16 Britannia. Twenty five pounds. (Previously listed as 4480). (1/4 oz. of fine gold).
R. Nathan design with textured background on the reverse, and with the inscription
'BRITANNIA 2016 1/4 OZ 999.9 FINE GOLD'
2016 — BU

BN17

BN17 Britannia. Twenty five pounds. (1/4 oz. of fine gold). R. A standing figure of Britannia
holding in her left hand a trident and in her right hand a shield with a lion in the background
and the inscription 'BRITANNIA 1/4 OZ FINE GOLD 2016 999.9'. (Reverse design:
Suzie Zamit)
2016 — Proof in gold *FDC* (0.9999) (Edition: 1,125 including coins in sets)

Obverse portrait by Raphael Maklouf

BO1

BO1   Britannia. Fifty pounds. (1/2oz of fine gold alloyed with copper). R. The figure of
Britannia standing upon a rock in the sea, her right hand grasping a trident and her left
hand resting on a shield and holding an olive branch, with the inscription '1/2 OUNCE
FINE GOLD BRITANNIA' and the year of the date. (Reverse design: Philip Nathan)

1987.. £650	1989 .... £650
— Proof *FDC* (Issued: 2,486).... £700	— Proof *FDC* (see PBS05)* £700
1988.. £650	
— Proof *FDC* (see PBS03)* £700	

* Coins marked thus were originally issued in Royal Mint sets.
NB. The spot price of gold at the time of going to press was £1030 per oz.

BO2

BO2 Britannia. Fifty pounds. (1/2oz of fine gold, alloyed with Silver). R. Britannia standing.

1990.. £650	1994 .... £650
— Proof *FDC* (see PBS07)*...... £700	— Proof *FDC* (see PBS11)*................. £700
1991.. £650	1995 .... £650
— Proof *FDC* (see PBS08)*...... £700	— Proof *FDC* (see PBS12)* £700
1992.. £650	1996 .... £650
— Proof *FDC* (see PBS09)*...... £700	— Proof *FDC* (see PBS13)* £700
1993.. £650	
— Proof *FDC* (see PBS10)*...... £700	

BO3 Britannia. Fifty pounds. (1/2 oz fine gold, alloyed with silver) 10th Anniversary of Britannia issue. R.The figure of Britannia standing in a chariot drawn along the seashore by two horses, with the word 'BRITANNIA' and the inscription 'HALF OUNCE FINE GOLD' and the date of the year. (Reverse design: Philip Nathan)
1997 Proof *FDC* (see PBS14)* £700

Obverse portrait by Ian Rank-Broadley

BO4   BO5

BO4 Britannia. Fifty pounds. (1/2 oz fine gold alloyed with silver). R. The figure of Britannia standing upon a rock in the sea, her right hand grasping a trident and her left hand resting on a shield and holding an olive branch, with the word 'BRITANNIA', the date of the year, and the inscription' 1/2 OUNCE FINE GOLD'. (Reverse design: Philip Nathan)

1998 Proof *FDC* (see PBS15)* £700	2002 Proof *FDC* (see PBS19)* £700
1999...£650	2004 Proof *FDC* (see PBS23)* £700
1999 Proof *FDC* (see PBS16)* £700	2006 Proof *FDC* (see PBS27)* £700
2000...£650	2012 Proof *FDC* (Edition: 1,000) £700
— Proof *FDC* (see PBS17)* £700	

BO5 Britannia. Fifty pounds. (1/2 oz fine gold alloyed with silver). R. The figure of Britannia, as guardian, with a shield in her left hand and a trident in her right hand, accompanied by a lion and, against the background of a wave motif, the words 'HALF OUNCE FINE GOLD' to the left and 'BRITANNIA' and the date of the year to the right. (Reverse design: Philip Nathan)

2001 ....£650	2001 Proof *FDC* (see PBS18)* £700

* Coins marked thus were originally issued in Royal Mint sets.
NB. The spot price of gold at the time of going to press was £1030 per oz.

BO6   BO8

BO6 **Britannia. Fifty pounds.** (1/2 oz fine gold alloyed with silver) R. Helmeted head of Britannia with, to the left, the word 'BRITANNIA' and, to the right, the inscription '1/2 OUNCE FINE GOLD' and the date of the year, the whole being overlaid with a wave pattern. (Reverse design: Philip Nathan)
2003...£650   2003 Proof *FDC* (see PBS20)* £700

BO7 **Britannia. Fifty pounds.** (1/2 oz fine gold alloyed with silver) R. Seated figure of Britannia facing to the left holding a trident with a shield at her side, with the word 'BRITANNIA', the inscription 'HALF OUNCE FINE GOLD' and the date of the year. (Reverse design: Philip Nathan)
2005 Proof *FDC* * £700

BO8 **Britannia. Fifty pounds.** (1/2 oz fine gold alloyed with silver) R. Seated figure of Britannia facing right holding a trident in her right hand and a sprig of olive in the left hand with a lion at her feet with the inscription 'HALF OUNCE FINE GOLD' and the word 'BRITANNIA' and the date of the year (See 4505) (Reverse design: Christopher Le Brun)
2007...£650   2007 Proof *FDC* (see PBS29)* £700

BO8A (½ oz platinum)
2007 Proof *FDC* * (see 2007 set, PPBCS1)...£800

BO9   B010   BO11

BO9 **Britannia. Fifty pounds.** (1/2 oz fine gold alloyed with silver) R. A Standing figure of Britannia holding a trident with a shield at her side, the folds of her dress transforming into a wave, with the word 'BRITANNIA' and the date of the year and the inscription '1/2 OUNCE FINE GOLD' (Reverse design: John Bergdahl)
2008 Proof *FDC* *......................... £700

BO9A (1/2 oz platinum)
2008 Proof *FDC* (see PPBCS2)* £800

BO10 **Britannia. Fifty pounds.** (1/2oz fine gold alloyed with silver) R.Standing figure of Britannia in horse drawn chariot.(see 4288 above)
2009...£650   2009 Proof *FDC* (see PBS31)* £700

BO11 **Britannia. Fifty pounds.** (1/2 oz fine gold alloyed with silver) R. A design depicting a profile bust of Britannia wearing a helmet, accompanied by the name 'BRITANNIA', the inscription '1/2 OUNCE FINE GOLD' and the date '2010' (Reverse design: Suzie Zamit)
2010 Proof *FDC* (Edition: 1,750 in sets)* £700

* Coins marked thus were originally issued in Royal Mint sets.
NB. The spot price of gold at the time of going to press was £1030 per oz.

BO12

BO12 Britannia. Fifty pounds. (1/2 oz fine gold alloyed with silver) R. A design depicting a seated figure of Britannia set against a background of a rippling Union Flag accompanied by the words ' 1/2 OUNCE FINE GOLD BRITANNIA, and the date '2011'. (Reverse design: David Mach)

2011 Proof *FDC* (Edition: 2,000 including coins in sets)*...£700

BO13 Britannia. Fifty pounds. (1/2 oz of fine gold) R. Seated figure of Britannia holding a trident with a shield at her side and an owl upon her knee with the word 'BRITANNIA' and the and the inscription '1/2 OUNCE FINE GOLD' and the date '2013' below the figure of Britannia. (Reverse design: Robert Hunt)

2013 — Proof in gold *FDC* (0.9999) (Edition: 525 including coins in sets)*

BO14

BO14 Britannia. Fifty pounds. (Previously listed as 4470). (1/2 oz of fine gold)..R. A design of the standing figure of Britannia baring a trident and shield, with a lion at her feet, set against the backdrop of a globe, and with the inscription 'BRITANNIA 999.9 1/2 OZ FINE GOLD 2014'. (Reverse design: Jody Clark)

2014 — Proof in gold *FDC* (0.9999) (Edition: 500 including coins in sets)*

BO15

BO15 Britannia. Fifty pounds. (1/2 oz. of fine gold).R. Design with textured background on the obverse and reverse, and with the inscription 'BRITANNIA 2015 1/2 OZ 999.9 FINE GOLD'.(Reverse design: Philip Nathan)

2015 — Bullion

* Coins marked thus were originally issued in Royal Mint sets.
NB. The spot price of gold at the time of going to press was £1030 per oz.

Obverse portrait by Jody Clark

BO16

BO16 Britannia. Fifty pounds. (1/2 oz. of fine gold). R. A figure of Britannia baring a trident and
shield, set against a backdrop of a sailing ship, cliffs and a lighthouse with the inscription
'BRITANNIA 1/2 OZ FINE GOLD 999.9 2015' (Reverse design: Antony Dufort)
2015 — Proof in gold *FDC* (0.9999) (Edition: 450 including coins in sets)*

BO17

BO17 Britannia. Fifty pounds. (1/2 oz. of fine gold). R. A standing figure of Britannia holding
in her left hand a trident and in her right hand a shield with a lion in the background and the
inscription 'BRITANNIA 1/2 OZ FINE GOLD 999.9 2016'. (Reverse design: Suzie Zamit)
2016 — Proof in gold *FDC* (0.9999) (Edition: 1,125 including coins in sets)

Obverse portrait by Raphael Maklouf

BP1

BP1 Britannia. One hundred pounds. (1oz of fine gold alloyed with copper) R. The figure
of Britannia standing upon a rock in the sea, her right hand grasping a trident and her left
hand resting on a shield and holding an olive branch, with the inscription 'ONE OUNCE
FINE GOLD BRITANNIA' and the year of the date. (Reverse design: Philip Nathan)

1987.. £1300	1989 .... £1300
— Proof *FDC* (Issued: 2,485).. £1350	— Proof *FDC* (Issued: 338) £1350
1988.. £1300	
— Proof *FDC* (Issued: 626)..... £1350	

* Coins marked thus were originally issued in Royal Mint sets.
NB. The spot price of gold at the time of going to press was £1030 per oz.

BP2 **Britannia. One hundred pounds.** (1oz of fine gold alloyed with silver) R. Britannia standing.

1990.. £1300	1994 .... £1300
— Proof *FDC* (Issued: 262)**. £1350	— Proof *FDC* (see PBS11)*................ £1350
1991.. £1300	1995 .... £1300
— Proof *FDC* (Issued: 143)**. £1350	— Proof *FDC* (see PBS12)* £1350
1992.. £1300	1996 .... £1300
— Proof *FDC* (see PBS09)*.... £1350	— Proof *FDC* (see PBS13)* £1350
1993.. £1300	
— Proof *FDC* (see PBS10)*.... £1350	

BP3

BP3 **Britannia. One Hundred pounds.** (1 oz of fine gold, alloyed with silver) 10th Anniversary of Britannia issue. R. The figure of Britannia standing in a chariot drawn along the seashore by two horses, with the word 'BRITANNIA', the inscription. 'ONE OUNCE FINE GOLD' and the date of the year. (Reverse design: Philip Nathan)

1997.. £1400   1997 Proof *FDC* (Issued: 164) £1600

Obverse portrait by Ian Rank-Broadley

BP4

BP4 **Britannia. One Hundred pounds.** (1oz fine gold alloyed with silver) R. The figure of Britannia standing upon a rock in the sea, her right hand grasping a trident and her left hand resting on a shield and holding an olive branch, with the word 'BRITANNIA', the date of the year, and the inscription' ONE OUNCE FINE GOLD'. (Reverse design: Philip Nathan)

1998 Proof *FDC* (see PBS15)*... £1350	2004 .... £1300
1999.. £1300	2004 Proof *FDC* (see PBS23)* £1350
1999 Proof *FDC* (see PBS16)*... £1350	2006 Proof *FDC* (see PBS27)* £1350
2000.. £1300	2012 .... £1300
2000 Proof *FDC* (see PBS17)*... £1350	2012 Proof *FDC* (see PBS36) £1500
2002 Proof *FDC* (see PBS19)*... £1350	

* Coins marked thus were originally issued in Royal Mint sets.
** Where numbers of coins are quoted, these refer to individual coins. Additional coins were included in sets which are listed in the appropriate section.
NB. The spot price of gold at the time of going to press was £1030 per oz.

BP5   BP6

BP4A (1 oz fine gold – 0.9999) R. As 4450 above
2013

BP4B (1 oz fine gold – 0.9999) R. As 4450 above but with revised inscription 'BRITANNIA
2014 1 oz 999.9 FINE GOLD'

BP5   **Britannia. One Hundred pounds.** (1oz fine gold alloyed with silver) R. The figure of Britannia,
as guardian, with a shield in her left hand and a trident in her right hand, accompanied by a lion
and, against the background of a wave motif, the words 'ONE OUNCE FINE GOLD' to the left
and 'BRITANNIA' and the date of the year to the right. (Reverse design: Philip Nathan)
2001.. £1300   2001 Proof *FDC* (see PBS18)* £1350

BP6   **Britannia. One Hundred pounds.** (1oz fine gold alloyed with silver) R. Helmeted head
of Britannia with, to the left, the word 'BRITANNIA' and, to the right, the inscription
'ONE OUNCE FINE GOLD' and the date of the year, the whole being overlaid with a
wave pattern. (Reverse design: Philip Nathan)
2003.. £1300   2003 Proof *FDC* (see PBS20)* £1350

BP7   BP8

BP7   **Britannia. One Hundred pounds.** (1oz fine gold alloyed with silver) R. Seated figure
of Britannia facing to the left holding a trident with a shield at her side, with the word
'BRITANNIA', the inscription 'ONE OUNCE FINE GOLD' and the date of the year.
(Reverse design: Philip Nathan)
2005 Proof *FDC* (see PBS25)* £1350

BP8   **Britannia. One Hundred pounds.** (1 oz fine gold alloyed with silver) R. Seated figure
of Britannia facing right holding a trident in her right hand and a sprig of olive in the left
hand with a lion at her feet with the inscription 'ONE OUNCE FINE GOLD' and the word
'BRITANNIA' and the date of the year (See 4505) (Reverse design: Christopher Le Brun)
2007.. £1300   2007 Proof *FDC* (see PBS29)* £1350

BP8A (1 oz platinum)
2007 Proof *FDC* (see 2007 set, PPBCS1)*..£1500

* Coins marked thus were originally issued in Royal Mint sets.
NB. The spot price of gold at the time of going to press was £1030 per oz.

BP9   BP10

BP9   Britannia. One Hundred pounds. (1oz fine gold alloyed with silver) R. A Standing figure
of Britannia holding a trident with a shield at her side, the folds of her dress transforming
into a wave, with the word 'BRITANNIA', and the date of the year, and the inscription
'ONE OUNCE FINE GOLD' (Reverse design: John Bergdahl)
2008... £1300   2008 Proof *FDC* (see PBS30)* £1350

BP9A (1 oz platinum)
2008 Proof *FDC* (see 2008 set, PPBCS2)*... £1500

BP10 Britannia. One Hundred pounds. (1oz fine gold alloyed with silver) R. Standing figure
of Britannia in horse drawn chariot.
2009... £1300   2009 Proof *FDC* (see PBS31)* £1350

BP11   BP12

BP11 Britannia. One Hundred pounds. (1oz fine gold alloyed with silver) R. A design
depicting a profile bust of Britannia wearing a helmet, accompanied by the name
'BRITANNIA', the inscription 'ONE OUNCE FINE GOLD' and the date '2010'.
(Reverse design: Suzie Zamit)
2010 .... £1300   2010 Proof *FDC* (Edition: 1,250 in sets)*£1350

BP12 Britannia. One Hundred pounds. (1 oz fine gold alloyed with silver) R. A design
depicting a seated figure of Britannia set against a background of a rippling Union Flag
accompanied by the words 'ONE OUNCE FINE GOLD BRITANNIA, and the date
'2011'. (Reverse design: David Mach)
2011 Proof *FDC (*Edition: 3,000 including coins in sets) * £1500

* Coins marked thus were originally issued in Royal Mint sets.
NB. The spot price of gold at the time of going to press was £1030 per oz.

BP13   BP14

BP13 Britannia. One Hundred pounds. (1 oz. of fine gold) R. Seated figure of Britannia
holding a trident with a shield at her side and an owl upon her knee with the word
'BRITANNIA' and 'ONE OUNCE FINE GOLD' and the date '2013' below the figure of
Britannia. (Reverse design: Robert Hunt)
2013 — Proof in gold *FDC* (0.9999) (Edition: 400 including coins in sets)*

BP14 Britannia. One Hundred pounds. (Previously listed as 4460). 1 oz of fine gold) R. A
design of the standing figure of Britannia baring a trident and shield, with a lion at her
feet, set against the backdrop of a globe, and with the inscription 'BRITANNIA 999.9
1 OZ FINE GOLD 2014'.(Reverse design: Jody Clark)
2014 — Proof in gold *FDC* (0.9999) (Edition: 400 including coins in sets)*

BP15

BP15 Britannia. One Hundred pounds. (1 oz. of fine gold). R. Design with textured
background on the obverse and reverse, and with the inscription 'BRITANNIA 2015
1 OZ 999.9 FINE GOLD'. (Reverse:design: Philip Nathan)
2015 — Bullion

Obverse portrait by Jody Clark

BP16

BP16 Britannia. One Hundred pounds. (1 oz of fine gold). R. A figure of Britannia
baring a trident and shield, set against a backdrop of a sailing ship, cliffs and a
lighthouse with the inscription 'BRITANNIA 1 OZ FINE GOLD 999.9 2015'
(Reverse design: Antony Dufort)
2015 – Proof in gold *FDC* (0.9999) (Edition: 400 including coins in sets)*

NB. The spot price of gold at the time of going to press was £1030 per oz.

BP17

BP17 Britannia. One Hundred pounds. (1 oz. of fine gold). R. Design with textured
background on the obverse and reverse, and with the inscription 'BRITANNIA 2016
1 OZ 999.9 FINE GOLD'   (Reverse: design: Philip Nathan)
2016 — Bullion

BP18

BP18 Britannia. One Hundred pounds. (1 oz. of fine gold) R. A standing figure of
Britannia holding in her left hand a trident and in her right hand a shield with a
lion in the background and the inscription 'BRITANNIA 1 OZ FINE GOLD 999.9
2016'. (Reverse design: Suzie Zamit)
2016 — Proof in gold *FDC* (0.9999) (Edition: 1,125 including coins in sets)

Obverse portrait by Ian Rank-Broadley

BQ1

BQ1 Britannia. Five Hundred pounds. (5 oz of fine gold) R. Seated figure of Britannia
holding a trident with a shield at her side and an owl upon her knee with the word
'BRITANNIA' and '5 OUNCES FINE GOLD' and the date '2013' below the figure of
Britannia. (Reverse design: Robert Hunt) (Reverse design: Robert Hunt)
2013 — Proof in gold *FDC* (0.9999) (Issued: 61) £8200

* Coins marked thus were originally issued in Royal Mint sets.
NB. The spot price of gold at the time of going to press was £1030 per oz

BQ2

BQ2 Britannia. Five Hundred pounds. (5 oz of fine gold) R A design of the standing figure
of Britannia baring a trident and shield, with a lion at her feet, set against the backdrop of
a globe, and with the inscription 'BRITANNIA 999.9 5 OZ FINE GOLD 2014'.(Reverse
design: Jody Clark)
2014 — Proof in gold *FDC* (0.9999) (Edition: 75)..£7500

BQ3

BQ3 Britannia. Five Hundred pounds. (5 oz 0.9999 fine gold) R. A standing figure of
Britannia holding in her left hand a trident and in her right hand a shield with a lion
in the background and the inscription 'BRITANNIA 5 OZ FINE GOLD 999.9 2016'.
(Reverse design: Suzie Zamit)
2016 — Proof in gold *FDC* (Edition: 55)

* Coins marked thus were originally issued in Royal Mint sets.
NB. The spot price of gold at the time of going to press was £1030 per oz.

Obverse portrait by Ian Rank-Broadley

5100

5100 **Two pounds.** (Previously listed as 4830). (1 oz 0.999 fine silver). R. A design depicting a horse prancing past the Uffington chalk white horse, with the inscription 'YEAR OF THE HORSE. 2014' and the Chinese symbol for horse. (Reverse design: Wuon-Gean Ho) 2014 — Proof in silver *FDC* (Edition: 8,888) £83

5100A Two pounds. Error obverse – known as a Mule. The obverse design of The Queen used for the £2 Silver Britannia uncirculated coin was paired with the reverse design of the Year of the Horse £2 silver coin.
2014

5100B   5101

5100B Two pounds. (1 oz 0.999 fine silver). R. Design as above but with the inscription 'YEAR OF THE HORSE 2014 1 OZ FINE SILVER 999'.
2014—Bullion

5101 **Two pounds.** (Previously listed as 4831). (1 oz 0.999 fine silver). R. Design depicting two Swaledale sheep, with the inscription 'YEAR OF THE SHEEP 2015' and the Chinese symbol for sheep. (Reverse design: Wuon-Gean Ho)
2015
— Proof in silver *FDC* (Edition: 9,888) £83
— Proof in silver with gold plating *FDC* (Edition: 4,888)...£110

5101A

5101A Two pounds. (1 oz 0.999 fine silver) R. Design as above but with the inscription 'YEAR OF THE SHEEP. 1oz FINE SILVER 999'.
2015—Bullion

Obverse portrait by Jody Clark

5102

5102 Two pounds. (1 oz. 0.999 fine silver). R. Design a monkey leaping through the trees with the inscription 'YEAR OF THE MONKEY 2016' and the Chinese symbol for monkeys. (Reverse design: Wuon-Gean Ho)
2016 — Proof in silver *FDC* (Edition: 8,054) £83

5102A   5103

5102A Two pounds. Reverse design as above but with inscription 'YEAR OF THE MONKEY.2016 1 OZ FINE SILVER 999'
2016 — Bullion (Edition: 138,888)

5103 Two pounds. (1 oz 0.999 fine silver). R. A depiction of a crowing rooster accompanied by a number of flowers with the inscription 'YEAR OF THE ROOSTER 2017 1 OZ FINE SILVER 999' and the Chinese symbol for a rooster. (Reverse design: Wuon-Gean Ho)
2017—Bullion
— Proof in silver *FDC* (Edition: 3,888) £85

Obverse portrait by Ian Rank-Broadley

5120

5120 Ten pounds. (Previously listed as 4840). (5 oz 0.999 fine silver). R. A design depicting a horse prancing past the Uffington chalk white horse, with the inscription 'YEAR OF THE HORSE. 2014' and the Chinese symbol for horse. (Reverse design: Wuon-Gean Ho) 2014 — Proof in silver *FDC* (Edition; 1,488) £450
Illustration shown at reduced size - actual coin diameter 65mm

5121

5121 Ten pounds. (Previously listed as 4841). (5 oz 0.999 fine silver). R. Design depicting two Swaledale sheep, with the inscription 'YEAR OF THE SHEEP 2015' and the Chinese symbol for sheep. (Reverse design: Wuon-Gean Ho) 2015
— Proof in silver *FDC* (Edition: 1,088) £395
Illustration shown at reduced size - actual coin diameter 65mm

Obverse portrait by Jody Clark

5122

5122 **Ten pounds.** (5 oz 0.999 fine silver). R. Design a monkey leaping through the trees with
the inscription 'YEAR OF THE MONKEY 2016' and the Chinese symbol for monkeys.
(Reverse design: Wuon-Gean Ho)
2016 — Proof in silver *FDC* (Edition: 588) £395
Illustration shown at reduced size - actual coin diameter 65mm

5123

5123 **Ten pounds.** (5 oz 0.999 fine silver). R. A depiction of a crowing rooster accompanied
by a number of flowers with the inscription 'YEAR OF THE ROOSTER 2017' and the
Chinese symbol for a rooster. (Reverse design: Wuon-Gean Ho)
2017 — BU (Edition: 388) £415
Illustration shown at reduced size - actual coin diameter 65mm

Obverse portrait by Ian Rank-Broadley

5140 **Five hundred pounds**. R. Design depicting two Swaledale sheep, with the inscription
'YEAR OF THE SHEEP 2015' and the Chinese symbol for sheep. (Reverse design:
Wuon-Gean Ho)
2015 — Proof in silver *FDC* (1 Kilo).

Obverse portrait by Jody Clark

5141

5141 **Five hundred pounds.** (1 kilo of fine silver). R. Design a monkey leaping through the
trees with the inscription 'YEAR OF THE MONKEY 2016' and the Chinese symbol for
monkeys. (Reverse design: Wuon-Gean Ho)
2016 — Proof in silver *FDC* (1 Kilo) (Edition: 88) £2,000
Illustration shown at reduced size – actual coin diameter 100mm

5142

5142 **Five hundred pounds.** (1 kilo 0.999 fine silver). R. A depiction of a crowing rooster
accompanied by a number of flowers with the inscription 'YEAR OF THE ROOSTER
2017' and the Chinese symbol for a rooster. (Reverse design: Wuon-Gean Ho)
2017 — Proof in silver *FDC* (Edition: 68) £2,050
Illustration shown at reduced size – actual coin diameter 100mm

Obverse portrait by Ian Rank-Broadley

5160   5161

5160 **Ten pounds.** (Previously listed as 4860). (1/10 oz 0.9999 fine gold). R. A design depicting a horse prancing past the Uffington chalk white horse, with the inscription 'YEAR OF THE HORSE. 2014' and the Chinese symbol for horse. (Reverse design: Wuon-Gean Ho)
2014 — BU (Edition; 2,888) £225

5161 **Ten pounds.** (Previously listed as 4861). (1/10 oz 0.9999 fine gold). R. Design depicting two Swaledale sheep, with the inscription 'YEAR OF THE SHEEP 2015' and the Chinese symbol for sheep. (Reverse design: Wuon-Gean Ho)
2015 — BU (Edition: 2,888) £225

Obverse portrait by Jody Clark

5162

5162 **Ten pounds.** (1/10 oz 0.999 fine gold). R. Design a monkey leaping through the trees with the inscription 'YEAR OF THE MONKEY 2016' and the Chinese symbol for monkeys. (Reverse design: Wuon-Gean Ho)
2016 — BU

5162A **Ten pounds.** (1/10 oz 0.9999 fine gold). R. Design a monkey leaping through the trees with the inscription 'YEAR OF THE MONKEY 2016 1 /10 OZ FINE GOLD 999.9' and the Chinese symbol for monkeys. (Reverse design: Wuon-Gean Ho)
2016 — BU (Edition: 1,888) £175

5163

5163 **Ten pounds.** (1/10 oz 0.9999 fine gold). R. A depiction of a crowing rooster accompanied by a number of flowers with the inscription 'YEAR OF THE ROOSTER 2017' and the Chinese symbol for a rooster. (Reverse design: Wuon-Gean Ho)
2017 — (Edition: 2,088) £205

NB. The spot price of gold at the time of going to press was £1030 per oz.

Obverse portrait by Ian Rank-Broadley

5180

5180   One hundred pounds. (Previously listed as 4870). (1 oz 0.9999 fine gold). R. A design depicting a horse prancing past the Uffington chalk white horse, with the inscription 'YEAR OF THE HORSE . 2014' and the Chinese symbol for horse. (Reverse design: Wuon-Gean Ho)

2014
— Gold bullion type (Edition: 30,000)
— Proof in gold *FDC* (Edition; 888)...£1950

5180A

5180A One hundred pounds. R. Design as above but the inscription 'YEAR OF THE HORSE · 2014 1 OZ fine gold 999.9'

2014 — Bullion

NB. The spot price of gold at the time of going to press was £1030 per oz

5181

5181 One hundred pounds. (Previously listed as 4871). (1 oz 0.999 fine gold). R. Design depicting two Swaledale sheep, with the inscription 'YEAR OF THE SHEEP 2015' and the Chinese symbol for sheep. (Reverse design: Wuon-Gean Ho)

2015 — Proof in gold *FDC* (Edition: 888)...£1950

5181A

5181A One hundred pounds. Reverse design as above but the inscription 'YEAR OF THE SHEEP . 2015 1 OZ fine gold 999.9'.

2015 — Bullion

Obverse portrait by Jody Clark

5182

5182 One hundred pounds. (1 oz 0.999 fine gold). R. Design a monkey leaping through the trees with the inscription 'YEAR OF THE MONKEY 2016' and the Chinese symbol for monkeys. (Reverse design: Wuon-Gean Ho)

2016 — Proof in gold *FDC* (Edition; 888)...£1,495

NB. The spot price of gold at the time of going to press was £1030 per oz

5183

5183 One hundred pounds. (1 oz 0.9999 fine gold). R. A depiction of a crowing rooster accompanied by a number of flowers with the inscription 'YEAR OF THE ROOSTER 2017 1 OZ FINE GOLD 999.9' and the Chinese symbol for a rooster. (Reverse design: Wuon-Gean Ho)

2017 — Proof in gold *FDC* (Edition: 688)...£1,795

Obverse portrait by Ian Rank-Broadley

5200 Five hundred pounds. (Previously listed as 4881). (5 oz. 0.9999 fine gold). R. A design depicting a horse prancing past the Uffington chalk white horse, with the inscription 'YEAR OF THE HORSE . 2014' and the Chinese symbol for horse. (Reverse design: Wuon-Gean Ho)

2014 — Proof in gold *FDC* (Edition:)...£7500

5201

5201 Five hundred pounds. (Previously listed as 4882). (5 oz. 0.9999 fine gold). R. Design depicting two Swaledale sheep, with the inscription 'YEAR OF THE SHEEP 2015' and the Chinese symbol for sheep. (Reverse design: Wuon-Gean Ho)

2015

— Proof in gold *FDC* (5 oz. fine gold) (Edition: 38) £7500

Illustration shown at reduced size - actual coin diameter 65mm

NB. The spot price of gold at the time of going to press was £1030 per oz.

Obverse portrait by Jody Clark

5202

5202 Five hundred pounds. (5 oz. 0.9999 fine gold). R. Design a monkey leaping through the
trees with the inscription 'YEAR OF THE MONKEY 2016' and the Chinese symbol for
monkeys. (Reverse design: Wuon-Gean Ho)
2016 — Proof in gold *FDC* (5 oz. fine gold) (Edition: 38)...£7,500
Illustration shown at reduced size - actual coin diameter 65mm

5203

5203 Five hundred pounds. (5 oz 0.9999 fine gold). R. A depiction of a crowing rooster
accompanied by a number of flowers with the inscription 'YEAR OF THE ROOSTER
2017' and the Chinese symbol for a rooster. (Reverse design: Wuon-Gean Ho)
2017 — Proof in gold *FDC* (Edition: 38)...£8,250
Illustration shown at reduced size - actual coin diameter 65mm

NB. The spot price of gold at the time of going to press was £1030 per oz.

Obverse portrait by Ian Rank-Broadley

5220

5220 One thousand pounds. (1 Kilo 0.9999 fine gold). R. Design depicting two Swaledale sheep, with the inscription 'YEAR OF THE SHEEP 2015' and the Chinese symbol for sheep.(Reverse design: Wuon-Gean Ho)
2015 — Proof in gold *FDC* (Edition:)..
Illustration shown at reduced size – actual coin diameter 100mm

Obverse portrait by Jody Clark

5221 One thousand pounds. (1 Kilo 0.9999 fine gold). R. Design a monkey leaping through the trees with the inscription 'YEAR OF THE MONKEY 2016' and the Chinese symbol for monkeys. (Reverse design: Wuon-Gean Ho)
2016 — Proof in gold *FDC* (Edition: 8)..£42,500

5222

5222 One thousand pounds. (1 kilo 0.9999 fine gold). R. A depiction of a crowing rooster accompanied by a number of flowers with the inscription 'YEAR OF THE ROOSTER 2017' and the Chinese symbol for a rooster. (Reverse design: Wuon-Gean Ho)
2017 — Proof in gold *FDC* (Edition: 8)..£49,995
Illustration shown at reduced size – actual coin diameter 100mm

NB. The spot price of gold at the time of going to press was £1030 per oz.

Obverse portrait by Jody Clark

QBA1

QBA1 Five pounds. R. A lion accompanied by a shield depicting Our Royal Arms with the inscription 'FINE SILVER 999.9 2016 LION OF ENGLAND 2OZ'. (Reverse design: Jody Clark)
2016

QBB1

QBB1 Twenty five pounds. R. A lion accompanied by a shield depicting Our Royal Arms with the inscription 'FINE GOLD 999.9 2016 LION OF ENGLAND 1/4OZ' (Reverse design: Jody Clark).
2016

QBC1

QBC1 One hundred pounds. R. A lion accompanied by a shield depicting Our Royal Arms with the inscription 'FINE GOLD 999.9 2016 LION OF ENGLAND 1OZ'. (Reverse design: Jody Clark).
2016

4850

4850 Five pound. (crown). (Previously listed as 4764). R. A design depicting British
troops waving to crowds as they embark on a ship with the inscription '1914 THE
FIRST WORLD WAR 1918. BEF' with the edge inscription 'SALUTE THE OLD
CONTEMPTIBLES'. (Reverse design: John Bergdahl)

2014 — Proof in silver *FDC* (Edition: 1,914 in sets, see PSS60)
— Proof in gold *FDC* (Edition: 20 in sets, see PGC16)

4851   4852

4851 Five pound. (crown). (Previously listed as 4765). R. A design depicting three Howitzers
with the inscription '1914 THE FIRST WORLD WAR 1918' and the edge inscription
'NEW AND FURIOUS BOMBARDMENT' (Reverse design: Edwina Ellis)

2014 — Proof in silver *FDC* (Edition: 1,914 in sets, see PSS60)
— Proof in gold *FDC* (Edition: 20 in sets, see PGC16)

4852 Five pound. (crown). R. A design depicting an effigy of Walter Tull in uniform with
soldiers walking out over no man's land and the inscription '1914 THE FIRST WORLD
WAR 1918' and 'WALTER TULL' around the coin, separated by poppy flowers with
barbed wire with the edge inscription 'A HERO ON AND OFF THE FIELD'. (Reverse
design: David Cornell)

2014 — Proof in silver *FDC* (Edition: 1,914 in sets, see PSS60)
— Proof in gold *FDC* (Edition: 20 in sets, see PGC16)

4853   4854

4853 Five pound. (crown). R. A design depicting a naval gun being loaded on board the deck of a battleship with the inscription '1914 THE FIRST WORLD WAR 1918. NAVY' and the edge inscription 'THE KING'S SHIPS WERE AT SEA'.(Reverse design: David Rowlands)

     2014 — Proof in silver *FDC* (Edition: 1,914 in sets, see PSS60)
          — Proof in gold *FDC* (Edition: 20 in sets, see PGC16)

4854 Five pound. (crown). R. A design depicting a man putting up propaganda posters onto a brick wall with the inscription '1914 THE FIRST WORLD WAR 1918' and the edge inscription 'FOLLOW ME! YOUR COUNTRY NEEDS YOU'

     2014 — Proof in silver *FDC* (Edition: 1,914 in sets, see PSS60)
          — Proof in gold *FDC* (Edition: 20 in sets, see PGC16)

4855

4855 Five pound. (crown). R. A design depicting a woman working fields with a plough with the inscription '1914 THE FIRST WORLD WAR 1918. HOMEFRONT' and the edge inscription 'SPEED THE PLOUGH AND THE WOMAN WHO DRIVES IT'. (Reverse design: David Rowlands)

     2014 — Proof in silver *FDC* (Edition: 1,914 in sets, see PSS60)
          — Proof in gold *FDC* (Edition: 20 in sets, see PGC16)

4856   4857

4856 Five pounds. (crown). R. A design of troops landing on the beaches below a map
showing the Gallipoli landings with the inscription '1914 THE FIRST WORLD
WAR 1918 – GALLIPOLI' with the edge inscription 'HEROES THAT SHED
THEIR BLOOD' (Reverse design : John Bergdahl)
2015 — Proof in silver *FDC* (Edition: 5,000 including coins in sets, see PSS66) *
       — Proof in gold *FDC* (Edition: 25 in sets, see PGC17)

4857 Five pounds. (crown). R. An effigy of Edith Cavell together with a nurse tending
a patient and the inscription '1914 THE FIRST WORLD WAS 1918' AND '
and 'EDITH CAVELL' around the coin, separated by poppy flowers attached
with barbed wire and the edge inscription 'SHE FACED THEM GENTLE AND
BOLD' (Reverse design: David Cornell)
2015 — Proof in silver *FDC* (Edition: 2,500 including coins in sets, see PSS69)...........£80
       — Proof in gold *FDC* (Edition: 25 in sets, see PGC17)

4858   4859

4858 Five pounds. (crown). R. An effigy of Albert Ball with First World War fighter
planes and the inscription '1914 THE FIRST WORLD WAR 1918' and 'ALBERT
BALL VC' around the coin , separated by poppy flowers attached with barbed wire
and with the edge inscription 'BY FAR THE BEST ENGLISH FLYING MAN'.
(Reverse design: David Cornell)
2015 — Proof in silver *FDC* (Edition:2,500 including coins in sets, see PSS66)
       — Proof in gold *FDC* (Edition: 25 in sets, see PGC17)

4859 Five pounds. (crown). R. A First World War submarine and the inscription '1914
THE FIRST WORLD WAR 1918'and the edge inscription 'IN LTTLE BOXES
MADE OF TIN' (Reverse design: David Rowlands)
2015 — Proof in silver *FDC* (Edition:2,500 including coins in sets, see PSS66)
       — Proof in gold *FDC* (Edition: 25 in sets, see PGC17)

NB. The spot price of gold at the time of going to press was £1030 per oz.

4860   4861

4860 **Five pounds.** (crown).R. A horse carrying munitions and a howitzer in the background
with the inscription '1914 THE FIRST WORLD WAR 1918' with the edge inscription
' PATIENT EYES COURAGEOUS HEARTS'. (Reverse design: David Lawrence)
2015 — Proof in silver *FDC* (Edition: 2,500 including coins in sets, see PSS66)
— Proof in gold *FDC* (Edition: 25 in sets, see PGC17)

4861 **Five pounds.** (crown). R. A sailor standing on deck below a red ensign with a ship in the
background and the inscription '1914 THE FIRST WORLD WAR 1918 MERCHANT
NAVY' and the edge inscription 'SEPULCHRED IN THE HARBOUR OF THE DEEP'
(Reverse design: Edwina Ellis)
2015 — Proof in silver *FDC* (Edition: 2,500 including coins in sets, see PSS69)
— Proof in gold *FDC* (Edition: 25 in sets, see PGC17)

Obverse portrait by Jody Clark

4862   4863

4862 **Five pounds.** R. Troops accompanying a tank across the battle field with the inscription
'1914 THE FIRST WORLD WAR 1918 SOMME' around the coin with the edge
inscription 'DEAD MEN CAN ADVANCE NO FURTHER' (Reverse design: John
Bergdah)
2016 — Proof in silver *FDC* (Edition: 6,000 including coins in sets) £80
— Proof in gold *FDC* (Edition: 25, see PGC19)

4863 **Five pounds.** R. An image of Jack Cornwell accompanied by an image of a naval gun
and a battleship with the inscription '1914 THE FIRST WORLD WAR 1918' and 'JACK
COMWELL VC' around the coin, separated by poppy flowers attached with barbed wire
and the edge inscription 'MOTHER , DON'T WATCH FOR POSTIE' (Reverse design:
David Cornell)
2016 — Proof in silver *FDC* (Edition: 2,000 including coins in sets)
— Proof in gold *FDC* (Edition: 25, see PGC19)

NB. The spot price of gold at the time of going to press was £1030 per oz.

4864   4865

4864   **Five pounds.** R. A depiction of battleships under fire and the inscription '1914 THE FIRST WORLD WAR 1918 JUTLAND' around the coin and the edge inscription ' OUR CHILDREN SHALL MEASURE THEIR WORTH' (Reverse design: John Bergdahl)

      2016 — Proof in silver *FDC* (Edition: 2,000) including coins in sets)

            — Proof in gold *FDC* (Edition:25, see PGC19)

4865   **Five pounds**. R. A line of troops walking across the battlefield accompanied by the inscription THERE SHALL BE IN THAT RICH EARTH A RICHER DUST CONCEALED' and the inscription '1914 THE FIRST WORLD WAR 1918' and the edge inscription 'THE TRUTH UNTOLD, THE PITY OF WAR' (Reverse design: David Lawrence)

      2016 — Proof in silver *FDC* (Edition: 6.000 including coins in sets) £80

            — Proof in gold *FDC* (Edition: 25, see PGC19)

4866   4867

4866   **Five pounds.** R. A group of soldiers sat in a trench and the inscription '1914 THE FIRST WORLD WAR 1918' 'ARMY' and the edge inscription 'MEN WHO MARCH AWAY'. (Reverse design: David Rowlands)

      2016 — Proof in silver *FDC* (Edition: 2,500 including coins in sets))

            — Proof in gold *FDC* (Edition: 25, see PGC19)

4867   **Five pounds.** R. A depiction of a naval gun on a Dreadnought and the inscription '1914 THE FIRST WORLD WAR 1918' and the edge inscription 'WATCH-DOGS OF THE NATION'. (Reverse design: Edwina Ellis)

      2016 — Proof in silver *FDC* (Edition: 2,000 including coins in sets))

            — Proof in gold *FDC* (Edition: 25, see PGC19)

NB. The spot price of gold at the time of going to press was £1030 per oz.

4890

4890 Ten pounds. (5 ounce). R. A line of troops walking across the battlefield accompanied by the inscription 'THERE SHALL BE IN THAT RICH EARTH A RICHER DUST CONCEALED' and the inscription '1914 THE FIRST WORLD WAR 1918' and the edge inscription 'THE TRUTH UNTOLD, THE PITY OF WAR' (Reverse design: David Lawrence)

2016 — Proof in silver *FDC* (Edition: 500) £395

　　　— Proof in gold *FDC* (Edition: 30)...£7,500

Illustration shown at reduced size – actual coin diameter 65mm

The Royal Mint issued a considerable number of coins to mark the London 2012 Olympic and Paralympic Games. It was decided that it would be easier for collectors if these coins were grouped together rather than be included with other coins of the same denomination. As a consequence the £2 coins issued in 2008 (previously listed as 4585 and 4586) have been renumbered and are now part of the Olympic group.

As part of their Programme of Olympic commemorative issues the Royal Mint has struck and released into circulation a series of 29 different 50 pence coins and details are given below. In addition to the circulating coins there is a series of numbered coin packs each containing the cupro-nickel versions of the coins but of higher quality. There are also sterling silver brilliant uncirculated examples.

The artist for each coin in the series has received a gold version of their design and a further example has been placed in the Mint museum. No value is shown at the present time.

       4960   4961

4960 Fifty pence. To commemorate the London 2012 Olympic and Paralympic Games. R. A design which depicts an athlete clearing a high jump bar, with the London 2012 logo above and the denomination '50 pence' below. (Reverse design: Florence Jackson)
2009
—   Specimen in presentation folder (Edition: 100,000) £3
—   Gold *FDC* – presented to the artist
2011 ....£1
—   Specimen in card (3/29) £3
—   Specimen in presentation folder signed by Daley Thompson (Edition: 500) £50
—   Specimen in presentation folder signed by Dame Kelly Holmes (Edition: 500) £50
—   Specimen in presentation folder signed by Lord Sebastian Coe (Edition: 500) £50
—   Silver BU (Edition: 30,000) £35

4961 Fifty pence. To commemorate the London 2012 Olympic and Paralympic Games. R. A design which depicts a cyclist in a velodrome, with the London Olympic logo above and the denomination '50 PENCE' below. (Reverse design: Theo Crutchley- Mack)
2010
—   Gold *FDC* – presented to the artist
2011..£1
Specimen in card (9/29)...£3
—   Silver BU (Edition: 30,000)...£35

4962 4963

4962 Fifty pence. To commemorate the London 2012 Olympic and Paralympic Games. ℞. A design which depicts a swimmer submerged in water, with the London Olympic logo above and the denomination '50 PENCE' below. (Reverse design: Jonathan Olliffe)
2011... £1   Specimen in card (1/29)................................£3
— Silver BU (Edition: 30,000)..... £35   — Gold *FDC* – presented to the artist

4963 Fifty pence. To commemorate the London 2012 Olympic and Paralympic Games. ℞. A design which depicts a bow being drawn, with the London Olympic logo above and the denomination '50 PENCE' below. (Reverse design: Piotr Powaga)
2011... £1   Specimen in card (2/29)...............................£3
— Silver BU (Edition: 30,000)..... £35   — Gold *FDC* – presented to the artist

4964 4965

4964 Fifty pence. To commemorate the London 2012 Olympic and Paralympic Games. ℞. A design which depicts a shuttlecock and a diagram of badminton actions, with the London Olympic logo above and the denomination '50 PENCE' below. (Reverse design: Emma Kelly)
2011... £1   Specimen in card (4/29)...............................£3
— Silver BU (Edition: 30,000)..... £35   — Gold *FDC* – presented to the artist

4965 Fifty pence. To commemorate the London 2012 Olympic and Paralympic Games. ℞. A design which depicts basketball players against a textured background of a large basketball, with the London Olympic logo above and the denomination '50 PENCE' below. (Reverse design: Sarah Payne)
2011... £1   Specimen in card (5/29)................................£3
— Silver BU (Edition: 30,000)..... £35   — Gold *FDC* – presented to the artist

4966   4967

4966 Fifty pence. To commemorate the London 2012 Olympic and Paralympic Games. R. A design which depicts a boccia player in a wheelchair throwing a ball, with the London Olympic logo above and the denomination "50 PENCE" below. (Reverse design: Justin Chung)
2011.. £1   Specimen in card (6/29)................................ £3
—   Silver BU (Edition: 30,000)..... £35   —   Gold *FDC* – presented to the artist

4967 Fifty pence. To commemorate the London 2012 Olympic and Paralympic Games. R. A design which depicts a pair of boxing gloves against the background of a boxing ring, with the London Olympic logo above and the denomination "50 PENCE" below. (Reverse design: Shane Abery)
2011.. £1   Specimen in card (7/29)................................ £3
—   Silver BU (Edition: 30,000)..... £35   —   Gold *FDC* – presented to the artist

4968   4969

4968 Fifty pence. To commemorate the London 2012 Olympic and Paralympic Games. R. A design which depicts a figure in a canoe on a slalom course, with the London Olympic logo above and the denomination "50 PENCE" below. (Reverse design: Timothy Lees)
2011.. £1   Specimen in card (8/29)................................ £3
—   Silver BU (Edition: 30,000)..... £35   —   Gold *FDC* – presented to the artist

4969 Fifty pence. To commemorate the London 2012 Olympic and Paralympic Games. R. A design which depicts a horse and rider jumping over a fence, with the London Olympic logo above and the denomination "50 PENCE" below. (Reverse design: Thomas Babbage)
2011.. £1   Specimen in card (10/29).............................. £3
—   Silver BU (Edition: 30,000)..... £35   —   Gold *FDC* – presented to the artist

4970   4971

4970 **Fifty pence.** To commemorate the London 2012 Olympic and Paralympic Games. R. A
design which depicts two figures fencing, with the London Olympic logo above and the
denomination "50 PENCE" below. (Reverse design: Ruth Summerfield)
2011..£1   Specimen in card (11/29)................................£3
—   Silver BU (Edition: 30,000).....£35   —   Gold *FDC* – presented to the artist

4971 **Fifty pence.** To commemorate the London 2012 Olympic and Paralympic Games. R. A
diagrammatic explanation of the offside rule in football, with the London Olympic logo above
and the denomination "50 PENCE" below. (Reverse design: Neil Wolfson)
2011..£1   Specimen in card (12/29)................................£3
—   Silver BU (Edition: 30,000).....£35   —   Gold *FDC* – presented to the artist

4972   4973

4972 **Fifty pence.** To commemorate the London 2012 Olympic and Paralympic Games. R. A
design which depicts a goalball player throwing a ball, with the London Olympic logo above
and the denomination "50 PENCE" below. (Reverse design: Jonathan Wren)
2011..£1   Specimen in card (13/29)................................£3
—   Silver BU (Edition: 30,000).....£35   —   Gold *FDC* – presented to the artist

4973 **Fifty pence.** To commemorate the London 2012 Olympic and Paralympic Games. R. A
design which depicts a gymnast with a ribbon, with the London Olympic logo above and the
denomination "50 PENCE" below. (Reverse design: Jonathan Olliffe)
2011..£1   Specimen in card (14/29)................................£3
—   Silver BU (Edition: 30,000).....£35   —   Gold *FDC* – presented to the artist

4974   4975

4974 Fifty pence. To commemorate the London 2012 Olympic and Paralympic Games. R. A design which depicts a handball player throwing a ball against a background of a handball court, with the London Olympic logo above and the denomination '50 PENCE' below. (Reverse design: Natasha Ratcliffe)

2011.. £1   Specimen in card (15/29)..............................£3
—   Silver BU (Edition: 30,000)..... £35   —   Gold *FDC* – presented to the artist

4975 Fifty pence. To commemorate the London 2012 Olympic and Paralympic Games. R. A design which depicts two hockey players challenging for the ball, with the London Olympic logo above and the denomination "50 PENCE" below. (Reverse design: Robert Evans)

2011.. £1   Specimen in card (16/29)..............................£3
—   Silver BU (Edition: 30,000)..... £35   —   Gold *FDC* – presented to the artist

4976   4977

4976 Fifty pence. To commemorave the London 2012 Olympic and Paralympic Games. R. A depiction of a judo throw, with the London Olympic logo above and the denomination '50 PENCE' below. (Reverse design: David Cornell)

2011.. £1   Specimen in card (17/29)..............................£3
—   Silver BU (Edition: 30,000)..... £35   —   Gold *FDC* – presented to the artist

4977 Fifty pence. To commemorate the London 2012 Olympic and Paralympic Games. R. A montage of the five sports which form the modern pentathlon, with the London Olympic logo above and the denomination '50 PENCE' below. (Reverse design: Daniel Brittain)

2011.. £1   Specimen in card (18/29)..............................£3
—   Silver BU (Edition: 30,000)..... £35   —   Gold *FDC* – presented to the artist

4978   4979

4978 **Fifty pence.** To commemorate the London 2012 Olympic and Paralympic Games. R̟. A
design which depicts a rowing boat accompanied by a number of words associated with the
Olympic movement, with the London Olympic logo above and the denomination '50 PENCE'
below. (Reverse design: David Podmore)

2011...£1
— Specimen in card (19/29)..£3
— Specimen in presentation folder signed by Sir Steve Redgrave (Edition: 500)............£50
— Silver BU (Edition: 30,000)...£35

4979 **Fifty pence.** To commemorate the London 2012 Olympic and Paralympic Games. R̟. A
design which depicts three sailing boats accompanied by a map of the coast of Weymouth,
with the London Olympic logo above and the denomination '50 PENCE' below. (Reverse
design: Bruce Rushin)

2011.. £1   Specimen in card (20/29).............................. £3
— Silver BU (Edition: 30,000)..... £35   — Gold *FDC* – presented to the artist

4980   4981

4980 **Fifty pence.** To commemorate the London 2012 Olympic and Paralympic Games. R̟. A design
which depicts a figure shooting, with the London Olympic logo above and the denomination
'50 PENCE' below. (Reverse design: Pravin Dewdhory)

2011.. £1   Specimen in card (21/29).............................. £3
— Silver BU (Edition: 30,000)..... £35   — Gold *FDC* – presented to the artist

4981 **Fifty pence.** To commemorate the London 2012 Olympic and Paralympic Games. R̟. A design
which depicts two table tennis bats against the background of a table and net, with the London
Olympic logo above and the denomination "50 PENCE" below. (Reverse design: Alan Linsdell)

2011.. £1   Specimen in card (22/29).............................. £3
— Silver BU (Edition: 30,000)..... £35   — Gold *FDC* – presented to the artist

4982   4983

4982 **Fifty pence.** To commemorate the London 2012 Olympic and Paralympic Games. R. A design which depicts two athletes engaged in Taekwondo, with the London Olympic logo above and the denomination "50 PENCE" below. (Reverse design: David Gibbons)

2011... £1   Specimen in card (23/29)..............................£3
— Silver BU (Edition: 30,000)..... £35   — Gold *FDC* – presented to the artist

4983 **Fifty pence.** To commemorate the London 2012 Olympic and Paralympic Games. R. A design which depicts a tennis net and tennis ball, with the London Olympic logo above and the denomination "50 PENCE" below. (Reverse design: Tracy Baines)

2011... £1   Specimen in card (24/29)..............................£3
— Silver BU (Edition: 30,000)..... £35   — Gold *FDC* – presented to the artist

4984   4985

4984 **Fifty pence.** To commemorate the London 2012 Olympic and Paralympic Games. R. A montage of the three sports which form the triathlon, with the London Olympic logo above and the denomination "50 PENCE" below. (Reverse design: Sarah Harvey)

2011... £1   Specimen in card (25/29)..............................£3
— Silver BU (Edition: 30,000)..... £35   — Gold *FDC* – presented to the artist

4985 **Fifty pence.** To commemorate the London 2012 Olympic and Paralympic Games. R. A design which depicts three figures playing beach volleyball, with the London Olympic logo above and the denomination "50 PENCE" below. (Reverse design: Daniela Boothman)

2011... £1   Specimen in card (26/29)..............................£3
— Silver BU (Edition: 30,000)..... £35   — Gold *FDC* – presented to the artist

4986   4987

4986 Fifty pence. To commemorate the London 2012 Olympic and Paralympic Games. R. A design which depicts the outline of a weightlifter starting a lift, with the London Olympic logo above and the denomination "50 PENCE" below. (Reverse design: Rob Shakespeare)

2011 ....£1   Specimen in card (27/29)............................£3
—   Silver BU (Edition: 30,000)...£35   —   Gold *FDC* – presented to the artist

4987 Fifty pence. To commemorate the London 2012 Olympic and Paralympic Games. R. A design which depicts a wheelchair rugby player in action, with the London Olympic logo above and the denomination "50 PENCE" below. (Reverse design: Natasha Ratcliffe)

2011 ....£1   Specimen in card (28/29)............................£3
—   Silver BU (Edition: 30,000)...£35   —   Gold *FDC* – presented to the artist

4988

4988 Fifty pence. To commemorate the London 2012 Olympic and Paralympic Games. R. A design which depicts two figures wrestling in a stadium, with the London Olympic logo above and the denomination "50 PENCE" below. (Reverse design: Roderick Enriquez)

2011 ....£1   Specimen in card (29/29)............................£3
—   Silver BU (Edition: 30,000)...£35   —   Gold *FDC* – presented to the artist

4951   4952

4951 **Two pounds.** (Previously listed as 4585) Centenary of the Olympic Games of 1908 held in London. R. A running track on which is superimposed the date '1908' accompanied by the denomination 'TWO POUNDS' and the date '2008', the whole design being encircled by the inscription 'LONDON OLYMPIC CENTENARY' with the edge inscription 'THE 4TH OLYMPIAD LONDON' (Reverse design: Thomas T Docherty)
2008 .... £5
 — Specimen in presentation folder (Issued: 29,594) £10
 — Proof *FDC* (in 2008 set, see PS93)* £15
 — Proof in Silver *FDC* (Issued: 8,023) £35
 — Proof piedfort in silver *FDC* (Edition: 5,000) £55
 — Proof in gold *FDC* (Issued: 1,908 including coins in sets) £700

4952 **Two pounds.** (Previously listed as 4586) London Olympic Handover Ceremony. R. The Olympic flag being passed from one hand to another, encircled by the inscription 'BEIJING 2008 LONDON 2012' and with the London 2012 logo below with the edge inscription 'I CALL UPON THE YOUTH OF THE WORLD' (Reverse design: Royal Mint Engraving Team)
2008 .... £5
 — Specimen in presentation folder (Edition: 250,000) £10
 — Proof in Silver *FDC* (Issued: 30,000) £38
 — Proof piedfort in silver *FDC* (Issued: 3,000) £60
 — Proof in gold *FDC* (Edition: 3,250 including coins in sets) £700

4953

4953 **Two pounds.** London to Rio Olympic Handover coin. R. A design which depicts a baton being passed from one hand to another, accompanied by the conjoined Union and Brazilian Flags. The reverse design is set against the background of a running track motif, with the London 2012 logo above and the surrounding inscription 'LONDON 2012 RIO 2016'. With the edge inscription 'I CALL UPON THE YOUTH OF THE WORLD'. (Reverse design: Jonathan Olliffe)
2012
 — Specimen in presentation card (Issued: 28,356) £10
 — Proof in silver *FDC* (Issued: 3,781) £60
 — Proof piedfort in silver *FDC* (Issued: 2,000) £105
 — Proof in gold *FDC* (Issued: 771) £1195

4920

4920 Five pounds. (crown) UK countdown to 2012 Olympic Games. R. In the centre a
depiction of two swimmers as faceted figures accompanied by the number '3' with
a section of a clock face to the right and the London 2012 logo to the left printed in
coloured ink on the precious metal versions and surrounded by a plan view of the main
Olympic Stadium incorporating the date '2009' with the words 'COUNTDOWN' above
and the inscription 'XXX OLYMPIAD' below. (Reverse design: Claire Aldridge) (Obv.
as 4556)

2009 (Edition: 500,000) £8
—   Specimen in presentation folder (Edition: 500,000) £10
—   Proof in silver *FDC* (Issued: 30,000)...£95
—   Proof piedfort in silver *FDC* (Issued: 6,000) £175
—   Proof in gold *FDC* (Edition: 4,000) £2000

4921

4921 Five pounds. (crown) UK countdown to 2012 Olympic Games. R. In the centre a
depiction of two runners as faceted figures accompanied by the number '2' with a section
of a clock face to the right and the London 2012 logo to the left printed in coloured
ink on the precious meta versions and surrounded by a plan view of the main Olympic
Stadium incorporating the date '2010' with the words 'COUNTDOWN' above and the
inscription 'XXX OLYMPIAD' below.(Reverse design: Claire Aldridge) (Obv. as 4556)

2010
—   Specimen in presentation card   (Edition: 250,000)...£8
—   Specimen in presentation folder (Edition: 250,000) £10
—   Proof in silver *FDC* (Edition: 30,000) £80
—   Proof piedfort in silver *FDC* (Edition: 4,000)..£200
—   Proof in gold *FDC* (Edition: 3,000) £2000

4922

4922 Five pounds. (crown) UK countdown to 2012 Olympic Games. R. In the centre a depiction of a cyclist as a faceted figure, accompanied by the number '1' with a section of a clock face to the right, below and to the left, and the London 2012 logo to the right printed in coloured ink on the precious metal versions and surrounded by a plan view of the main Olympic Stadium incorporating the date '2011' with the words 'COUNTDOWN' above and the inscription 'XXX OLYMPIAD' below. (Reverse design: Claire Aldridge)

2011
— Specimen in presentation card (Edition: 250,000) £8
— Specimen in presentation folder (Edition: 250,000)..£10
— Proof in silver *FDC* (Edition: 30,000) £100
— Proof piedfort in silver *FDC* (Edition: 4,000) £175
— Proof in gold *FDC* (Edition: 3,000)...£2880

4923

4923 Five pounds. (crown) UK countdown to 2012 Olympic Games. R. A depiction of three athletes as faceted figures standing on a victory podium, with a section of a clock-face to the right, to the left and above, and the London 2012 logo to the right. The reverse design is surrounded by a plan view of the main Olympic Stadium, incorporating the date '2012' at the top, and the word 'COUNTDOWN' above and the inscription 'XXX OLYMPIAD' below. (Reverse design: Claire Aldridge)

2012
— Specimen in presentation card (Edition: 250,000) £8
— Specimen in presentation folder (Edition: 250,000) £13
— Proof in silver *FDC* (Issued: 12,670)..£100
— Proof piedfort in silver *FDC* (Issued: 2,324) £175
— Proof in gold *FDC* (Issued: 1,007)...£2880

4924

4924 Five pounds. (crown) The London 2012 Olympic Games. ℞. An image of the skyline of
some of the most well-known landmarks and buildings in London reflected in the River
Thames, with the inscription 'LONDON 2012' above. Surrounding the skyline image is
a selection of sports from the London 2012 Games with the London 2012 logo at the top.
(Reverse design: Saiman Miah)
2012
— Specimen in presentation folder.. £15
— Proof in silver *FDC* (Edition: 100,000) £100
— Proof in silver with gold plating *FDC* (Edition: 12,500)....................................£125
— Proof piedfort in silver *FDC* (Edition: 7,000)...£175
— Proof in gold *FDC* (Edition: 5,000) £2880

4925

4925 Five pounds. (crown) The London 2012 Paralympic Games. ℞. A design showing
segments of a target, a spoked wheel, a stopwatch and the clock face of the Palace of
Westminster. The inscription 'LONDON 2012' appears on the target and the London
2012 Paralympic logo appears on the stopwatch. On the gold and silver coins the London
Paralympic logo will be printed in coloured ink , while on the cupro-nickel coin the logo
will be struck into the surface. (Reverse design: Pippa Anderson)
2012
— Specimen in presentation folder (Edition: 250,000) £15
— Proof in silver *FDC* (Edition: 10,000) £100
— Proof in silver with gold plating *FDC* (Edition: 3,000).....................................£125
— Proof piedfort in silver *FDC* (Edition: 2,012)..£175
— Proof in gold *FDC* (Edition: 2,012) £2880

4930

4930 **Five pounds.** (crown) The Mind of Britain. R. A depiction of the clock-face of the Palace of Westminster accompanied by the London 2012 logo, printed in coloured ink and a quotation From Walter Bagehot, 'NATIONS TOUCH AT THEIR SUMMITS'. (Reverse design: Shane Greeves and the Royal Mint Engraving Department)
2009
— Proof *FDC* (Edition: 100,000)£20 — Proof silver *FDC* (Edition: 95,000) £100

4931

4931 **Five pounds.** (crown). The Mind of Britain. R. A depiction of Stonehenge accompanied by the London 2012 logo, printed in coloured ink on the silver version and a quotation from William Blake 'GREAT THINGS ARE DONE WHEN MEN AND MOUNTAINS MEET' (Reverse design: Shane Greeves and the Royal Mint Engraving Department)
2009
— Proof silver *FDC* (Edition: 95,000) £100

4932   4933

4932 Five pounds. (crown). The Mind of Britain. ℞. A depiction of the Angel of the North
accompanied   by the London 2012 logo printed in coloured ink on the silver version and a
quotation from William Shakespeare 'I HAVE TOUCHED THE HIGHEST POINT OF MY
GREATNESS' (Reverse design: Shane Greeves and the Royal Mint Engraving Department)
2009

—   Proof silver *FDC* (Edition: 95,000) £100

4933 Five pounds. (crown). The Mind of Britain. ℞. A depiction of the Flying Scotsman
accompanied   by the London 2012 logo printed in coloured ink on the silver version and
a quotation from William Shakespeare 'TRUE HOPE IS SWIFT' (Reverse design:
Shane Greeves and the Royal Mint Engraving Department)
2009

—   Proof silver *FDC* (Edition: 95,000) £100

4934

4934 Five pounds. (crown). The Mind of Britain. ℞. A depiction of Eduardo Paolozzi's
sculpture of Isaac Newton North accompanied by the London 2012 logo printed in
coloured ink on the silver version and a quotation from William Shakespeare 'MAKE
NOT YOUR THOUGHTS YOUR PRISONS' (Reverse design: Shane Greeves and the
Royal Mint Engraving Department)
2009

—   Proof silver *FDC* (Edition: 95,000) £100

4935

4935 Five pounds. (crown). The Mind of Britain. ℞. A depiction of the Globe Theatre
accompanied by the London 2012 logo printed in coloured ink on the silver version and a
quotation from William Shakespeare 'WE ARE SUCH STUFF AS DREAMS ARE MADE
ON' (Reverse design: Shane Greeves and the Royal Mint Engraving Department)
2009
—   Proof silver *FDC* (Edition: 95,000) £100

4936   4937

4936 Five pounds. (crown). The Body of Britain. ℞. A depiction of Rhossili Bay accompanied
by the London 2012 logo printed in coloured ink, and a quotation from William Blake
'TO SEE A WORLD IN A GRAIN OF SAND' (Reverse design: Shane Greeves and the
Royal Mint Engraving Department)
2010
—   Proof silver *FDC* (Edition: 95,000) £100

4937 Five pounds. (crown). The Body of Britain ℞. A depiction of Giant's Causeway
accompanied by the London 2012 logo printed in coloured ink, and a quotation from
Alice Oswald 'WHEN THE STONE BEGAN TO DREAM' (Reverse design: Shane
Greeves and the Royal Mint Engraving Department)
2010
—   Proof silver *FDC* (Edition: 95,000) £100

4938   4939

4938 **Five pounds.** (crown). The Body of Britain R. A depiction of the River Thames accompanied
by the London 2012 logo printed in coloured ink, and a quotation from Percy Bysshe Shelley,
'TAMELESS, AND SWIFT AND PROUD' (Reverse design: Shane Greeves and the Royal
Mint Engraving Department)
2010
— Proof silver *FDC* (Edition: 95,000)...£100

4939 **Five pounds.** (crown). The Body of Britain. R. A depiction of a barn owl accompanied by
the London 2012 logo printed in coloured ink, and a quotation from Samuel Johnson 'THE
NATURAL FLIGHTS OF THE HUMAN MIND' (Reverse design: Shane Greeves and the
Royal Mint Engraving Department)
2010
— Proof silver *FDC* (Edition: 95,000)...£100

4940   4941

4940 **Five pounds.** (crown). The Body of Britain. R. A depiction of oak leaves and an acorn
accompanied by the London 2012 logo printed in coloured ink, and a quotation from Alfred,
Lord Tennyson, 'TO STRIVE, TO SEEK......AND NOT TO YIELD' (Reverse design: Shane
Greeves and the Royal Mint Engraving Department)
2010
— Proof silver *FDC* (Edition: 95,000)...£100

4941 **Five pounds.** (crown). The Body of Britain. R. A depiction of a weather-vane accompanied by
the London 2012 logo printed in coloured ink, and a quotation from Charlotte Bronte, NEVER
MAY A CLOUD COME O'ER THE SUNSHINE OF YOUR MIND' (Reverse design:
Shane Greeves and the Royal Mint Engraving Department)
2010
— Proof silver *FDC* (Edition: 95,000)...£100

4942   4943

4942   **Five pounds.** (crown). The Spirit of Britain. R. A depiction of the intertwined national emblems
of England, Scotland, Wales and Northern Ireland accompanied by the London 2012 logo, printed
in coloured ink, and a quotation from John Lennon, 'AND THE WORLD WILL BE ONE'
(Reverse design: Shane Greeves and the Royal Mint Engraving Department)
2010
—   Proof silver *FDC* (Edition: 95,000)... £100

4943   **Five pounds.** (crown).The Spirit of Britain. R. A depiction of the White Rabbit from Lewis
Carroll's *Alice in Wonderland* accompanied by the London 2012 logo, printed in coloured ink,
and a quotation from T S Eliot, 'ALL TOUCHED BY A COMMON GENIUS' (Reverse design:
Shane Greeves and the Royal Mint Engraving Department)
2010
—   Proof silver *FDC* (Edition: 95,000)... £100

4944   4945

4944   **Five pounds.** (crown).The Spirit of Britain. R. A view down the Mall of cheering crowds
accompanied by the London 2012 logo, printed in coloured ink, and a quotation from Alfred,
Lord Tennyson, 'KIND HEARTS ARE MORE THAN CORONETS' (Reverse design: Shane
Greeves and the Royal Mint Engraving Department)
2010
—   Proof *FDC* (Edition; 100,000)..£20
—   Proof silver *FDC* (Edition: 95,000)... £100

4945   **Five pounds.** (crown).The Spirit of Britain. R. A DEPICTION OF THE STATUE OF Winston
Churchill in Parliament Square accompanied by the London 2012 logo, printed in coloured ink,
and a quotation from Anita Roddick, 'BE DARING, BE FIRST, BE DIFFERENT, BE JUST'
(Reverse design: Shane Greeves and the Royal Mint Engraving Department)
2010
—   Proof *FDC* (Edition; 100,000)..£20
—   Proof silver *FDC* (Edition: 95,000)... £100

4946

4946 Five pounds. (crown).The Spirit of Britain. ℞ An arrangement of musical instruments based on a well known sculpture accompanied by the London 2012 logo, printed in coloured ink, and a quotation from John Lennon and Paul McCartney, 'ALL YOU NEED IS LOVE'. (Reverse design: Shane Greeves and the Royal Mint Engraving Department) 2010
   —   Proof silver *FDC* (Edition: 95,000) £100

4947

4947 Five pounds. (crown).The Spirit of Britain. ℞. An image of the nineteenth-century anti-slavery campaigner Equiano accompanied by the London 2012 logo, printed in coloured ink, and a quotation from William Shakespeare, 'TO THINE OWN SELF BE TRUE'. (Reverse design: Shane Greeves and the Royal Mint Engraving Department) 2010
   —   Proof silver *FDC* (Edition: 95,000) £100

4950

4950 Ten pounds. (Five ounce). ℞. A design of the winged horse Pegasus rearing on its hind legs surrounded by the inscription 'LONDON OLYMPIC GAMES', and the London 2012 logo and the date '2012'.(Reverse design: Christopher Le Brun)
2012
— Proof in 0.999 fine silver *FDC* (Issued: 5,056) £525
— Proof in 0.999 fine gold *FDC* (Issued: 193)... £11500
Illustration shown at reduced size – actual coin diameter 65 mm.

4905

4905 Twenty five pounds. Faster. ℞. An image of Diana accompanied by a depiction of the sport of cycling, specifically pursuit racing ,with Olympic Rings above, the name 'DIANA' to the left, the Latin word for faster 'CITIUS', to the right, and the inscription 'LONDON 2012' below. (Reverse design: John Bergdahl)
2010
— Proof in gold *FDC* (Edition: 20,000) £600

4906

4906 Twenty five pounds. Faster. ℞. An image of Mercury accompanied by a depiction of the sport of running, with Olympic Rings above, the name 'MERCURY' to the left, the Latin word for faster 'CITIUS', to the right, and the inscription 'LONDON 2012' below. (Reverse design: John Bergdahl)
2010
— Proof in gold *FDC* (Edition: 20,000).. £600

4907

4907 **Twenty five pounds.** Higher. ℞. An image of Apollo accompanied by a depiction of the sport of rhythmic gymnastics, with Olympic Rings above, the name 'APOLLO' to the left, the Latin word for higher 'ALTIUS', to the right, and the inscription 'LONDON 2012' below. (Reverse design: John Bergdahl)
2011
—   Proof in gold *FDC* (Edition: 20,000 including coins in sets)..............................£600

4908   4909   4910

4908 **Twenty five pounds.** Higher. ℞. An image of Juno accompanied by a depiction of the sport of pole vaulting, with Olympic Rings above, the name 'JUNO' to the left, the Latin word for higher 'ALTIUS', to the right, and the inscription 'LONDON 2012' below. (Reverse design: John Bergdahl)
2011
—   Proof in gold *FDC* (Edition: 20,000 including coins in sets)..............................£600

4909 **Twenty five pounds.** Stronger. ℞. An image of Vulcan accompanied by a depiction of the sport of hammer throwing, with the Olympic Rings above, the name 'VULCAN' to the left, and the Latin word for stronger 'FORTIUS', to the right, and the inscription 'LONDON 2012' below. (Reverse design: John Bergdahl)
2012
—   Proof in gold *FDC* (Edition: 20,000 including coins in sets)..............................£600

4910 **Twenty five pounds.** Stronger. ℞. An image of Minerva accompanied by a depiction Of the sport of javelin throwing, with the Olympic Rings above, the name 'MINERVA' to the left , the Latin word for stronger, 'FORTIUS', to the right, and the inscription 'LONDON 2012@ below. (Reverse design: John Bergdahl)
2012
—   Proof in gold *FDC* (Edition: 20,000 including coins in sets)..............................£600

4915

4915 One hundred pounds. Faster. R. An image of Neptune, accompanied by a depiction of
the sport of sailing, with the Olympic Rings above, the name 'NEPTUNE' to the left, the
Latin word for faster 'CITIUS' to the right, and the inscription 'LONDON 2012' below.
(Reverse design: John Bergdahl)
2010
— Proof in gold *FDC* (Edition: 7,500 including coins in sets)..............................£2300

4916

4916 One hundred pounds. Higher. R. An image of Jupiter, accompanied by a depiction of
the sport of diving, with the Olympic Rings above, the name 'JUPITER' to the left,
the Latin word for higher 'ALTIUS' to the right, and the inscription 'LONDON 2012'
below. (Reverse design: John Bergdahl)
2011
— Proof in gold *FDC** (Edition: 7,500 including coins in sets)............................£2300

4917

4917 One hundred pounds. Stronger. R. An image of Mars accompanied by a depiction of the
sport of boxing, with the Olympic Rings above, the name 'MARS' to the left, the Latin
word for stronger, 'FORTIUS', to the right, and the inscription 'LONDON 2012' below.
(Reverse design: John Bergdahl)
2012
— Proof in gold *FDC* (Edition: 7,500 including coins in sets) £2300

4920

4918 Five hundred pounds. (One kilo). R. A design consisting of celebratory pennants and the
inscription 'XXX OLYMPIAD' surrounded by the epigram 'UNITE OUR DREAMS TO
MAKE THE WORLD A TEAM OF TEAMS' (Reverse design: Tom Phillips)
2012
—   Proof in silver (Issued: 910)..£3000
Illustration shown at reduced size – actual coin diameter 100 mm

4921

4919 One thousand pounds. (One kilo). R. A design depicting individual pieces of sporting
equipment encircled by a laurel of victory. (Reverse design: Sir Anthony Caro)
2012
—   Proof in gold (Issued: 20)..£100000
Illustration shown at reduced size – actual coin diameter 100 mm

The practice of issuing annual sets of coins was started by the Royal Mint in 1970 when a set of the £SD coins was issued as a souvenir prior to Decimalisation. There are now regular issues of brilliant uncirculated coin sets as well as proofs in base metal, and issues in gold and silver. In order to simplify the numbering system, and to allow for the continuation of the various issues in the future, the Prefix letters have been changed. The base metal proof sets will continue the series of numbers from the 1970 set, PS20. Other sets, such as those of uncirculated coins, silver and gold now have their numbering series commencing with number 01 in each case.

In addition to the annual sets of uncirculated and proofs coins sold by the Royal Mint to collectors and dealers, the Mint has produced specially packaged sets and single coins for companies. No details are made available of these issues and therefore no attempt has been made to include them in the listings below. The Mint also sells 'Christening' and 'Wedding' sets in distinctive packaging but the numbers circulating in the market are relatively modest and of limited appeal after the year of issue.

The Mint has recently offered sets of coins to collectors that consist of coins obtained from the market e.g. silver proofs, crowns and gold sovereigns showing different portraits. Although these are available in limited numbers from the Mint, it has been decided not to list them in the section devoted to sets.

Following the comprehensive review of the layout, it has been decided to move the folder containing the two 50 pence coins of 1992 to the list below of uncirculated coins. This was formerly included as 4352A, and is now US13 with all subsequent numbers adjusted by one.

Uncirculated Sets   £

US01–**1982**	Uncirculated (specimen) set in Royal Mint folder, 50p to ½p, new reverse type, including 20 pence (Issued: 205,000)...	(7)	9
US02–**1983**	'U.K.' £1 (4221) to ½p (Issued: 637,100)...	(8)	15
US03–**1984**	'Scottish' £1 (4222) to ½p (Issued: 158,820)...	(8)	15
US04–**1985**	'Welsh' £1 (4331) to 1p, new portrait of The Queen (Issued: 102,015)..........	(7)	15
US05–**1986**	'Commonwealth Games' £2 (4311) plus 'Northern Irish' £1 (4332) to 1p, (Issued: 167,224)..	(8)	18
US06–**1987**	'English' £1 (4333) to 1p, (Issued: 172,425)..	(7)	15
US07–**1988**	'Arms' £1 (4334) to 1p, (Issued: 134,067)..	(7)	15
US08–**1989**	'Scottish' £1 (4335) to 1p, (Issued: 77,569)...	(7)	20
US09–**1989**	'Bill of Rights' and 'Claim of Right' £2s (4312 and 4313) in Royal Mint folder (Issued: not known)...	(2)	25
US10–**1990**	'Welsh' £1 (4331) to 1p plus new smaller 5p, (Issued: 102,606)...................	(8)	20
US11–**1991**	'Northern Irish' £1 (4332) to 1p, (Issued: 74,975).......................................	(7)	20
US12–**1992**	'English' £1 (4333), 'European Community' 50p (4352) and 'Britannia' 50p, 20p to 1p plus new smaller 10p (Issued: 78,421)...	(9)	25
US13-**1992**	'European Community' 50p (4352) and 'Britannia' 50p (4351) in presentation folder previously listed as 4352A..	(2)	20
US14–**1993**	'UK' £1 (4336), 'European Community' 50p (4352) to 1p ((Issued: 56,945)	(8)	25
US15–**1994**	'Bank of England' £2 (4314), 'Scottish' £1 (4337) and 'D-Day' 50p (4353) to 1p, (Issued: 177,971)...	(8)	15
US16–**1995**	'Peace' £2 (4315) and 'Welsh' £1 (4338) to 1p (Issued: 105, 647).................	(8)	15
US17–**1996**	'Football' £2 (4317) and 'Northern Irish' £1 (4339) to 1p (Issued: 86,501)...	(8)	15
US18–**1997**	'Bimetallic' £2 (4318), 'English' £1 (4340) to 1p plus new smaller 50p (Issued: 109,557)..	(9)	15
US19–**1998**	'Bimetallic' £2 (4570), 'UK' £1 (4590) and 'EU' 50 pence (4611) to1 pence (Issued: 96,192)...	(9)	25
US20–**1998**	'EU' and 'Britannia' 50 pence (4611 and 4610) in Royal Mint folder............	(2)	6
US21–**1999**	'Bimetallic' 'Rugby' £2 (4571), 'Scottish' £1 (4591) to 1p (Issued: 136,696)	(8)	18
US22–**2000**	'Bimetallic' £2 (4570), 'Welsh' £1 (4592) to 1p plus 'Library' 50 pence (4613) (Issued: 117,750)	(9)	18
US23–**2001**	'Bimetallic' £2 (4570), 'Bimetallic' 'Marconi' £2 (4572), 'Irish' £1 (4594) to 1p (Issued: 57,741)..	(9)	18

£

US24–**2002**	'Bimetallic' £2 (4570), 'English' £1 (4594) to 1p (Issued: 60,539)............... (8)	18
US25–**2002**	'Bimetallic' £2 Commonwealth Games set of four (4573, 4574, 4575 and 4576) (Issued: 47,895)....................... (4)	45
US26–**2003**	Bimetallic 'DNA' £2 (4577), 'Bimetallic' £2 (4570), 'UK' £1 (4590), 'Suffragette' 50 pence (4614) and 'Britannia' 50 pence (4610) to 1p. (Issued: 62,741)............................... (10)	28
US27–**2004**	'Bimetallic' 'Penydarren engine' £2 (4578), 'Bimetallic' £2 (4570), 'Forth Rail Bridge' £1 (4595), 'Sub four-minute mile' 50 pence (4615) and 'Britannia' 50 pence (4610) to1p. (Issued: 46,032)...................... (10)	28
US28–**2004**	'Bimetallic' 'Penydarren engine' £2 (4578), 'Forth Rail Bridge' £1(4595), 'Sub four-minute mile' 50 pence (4615). (Issued: 14,391)...................... (3)	10
US29–**2005**	'Bimetallic' 'Gunpowder Plot' £2 (4579), 'Bimetallic' £2 (4570), 'Menai Straits Bridge' £1 (4596), 'Samuel Johnson's Dictionary' 50 pence (4616) and 'Britannia' 50 pence (4610) to 1p. (Issued: 51,776).................... (10)	20
US30–**2005**	'Bimetallic' 'Gunpowder Plot' £2 (4579), 'Menai Straits Bridge' £1 (4596), 'Samuel Johnson's Dictionary' 50 pence (4616)........................ (3)	10
US31–**2005**	'Trafalgar' £5, struck in c/n (4559) and 'Nelson' £5 struck in c/n (4560) ...... (2)	25
US32–**2006**	'Bimetallic' 'Isambard Brunel' £2 (4581), 'Bimetallic' 'Paddington Station' £2 (4582), 'MacNeill's Egyptian Arch' £1 (4597), 'Victoria Cross' 50 pence (4617), 'Wounded soldier' 50 pence (4618) to 1p (Issued: 74,231).................... (10)	28
US33–**2006**	'Bimetallic' 'Isambard Brunel' £2 (4581), 'Bimetallic' 'Paddington Station' £2 (4582)....................... (2)	10
US34–**2006**	'Victoria Cross' 50 pence (4617), 'Wounded soldier' 50 pence (4618)......... (2)	8
US35–**2007**	'Bimetallic' 'Act of Union' £2 (4583), 'Bimetallic' 'Abolition of Slave Trade' £2 (4584), 'Gateshead Millennium Bridge' £1 (4598), 'Scouting Movement' 50 pence (4619), to 1p (Issued: 91,878)........................ (9)	24
US36–**2008**	'Bimetallic' 'London Olympics Centenary' £2 (4951), 'Bimetallic' £2 (4570), 'UK' £1 (4590), 'Britannia' 50 pence (4610), to 1p (Issued: 79,118)............. (9)	20
US37–**2008**	'Emblems of Britain', 'UK' £1 (4590), 'Britannia' 50 pence (4610), and 20 pence to 1 p (Issued: 57,126)....................... (7)	12
US38–**2008**	'The Royal Shield of Arms', 'Royal Shield' £1 (4604) to1p (4611, 4631, 4651, 4671, 4691, 4711) (Issued: 100,000)........................ (7)	16
US39–**2009**	'Bimetallic' 'Charles Darwin' £2 (4586), Bimetallic 'Robert Burns' £2 (4585) 'Bimetallic'£2 (4570), 'Royal Shield' £1 (4604), 50 pence 'Kew Gardens' (4621) 50 pence (4620), 20 pence (4631), 10 pence (4651), 5 pence (4671), 2 pence (4691) and 1 pence (4711) (Edition: 100,000)................................ (11)	22
US40- **2009**	'Bimetallic'£2 (4570), 'Royal Shield' £1 (4604), 50 pence 'Kew Gardens' (4621) 50 pence (4620), 20 pence (4631), 10 pence (4651), 5 pence (4671), 2 pence (4691) and 1 pence (4711) .... (8)	15
US41- **2009**	'Royal Shield' £1 (4604), 50 pence (4620), 20 pence (4631), 10 pence (4651), 5 pence (4671), 2 pence (4691) and 1 pence (4711)..................... (7)	15
US42–**2010**	'Bimetallic 'Florence Nightingale' £2 (4587), 'Bimetallic'£2 (4570), 'London' £1 (4605), 'Belfast' £1 (4606), 'Royal Shield '£1(4604), 50 pence 'Girl Guiding' (4626), 50 pence (4620), 20 pence (4631), 10 pence (4651), 5 pence (4671), 2 pence (4691) and 1 pence (4711) (Edition: 50,000)....... (12)	25
US43–**2010**	'Bimetallic'£2 (4570), 'Royal Shield' £1 (4604), 50 pence (4620), 20 pence (4631), 10 pence (4651), 5 pence (4671), 2 pence (4691) and 1 pence (4711) (8)	15
US44–**2010**	'London' £1 (4605) and 'Belfast' £1 (4606) (Edition: 10,000) .... (2)	13
US45–**2011**	'Bimetallic' 'Mary Rose' £2 (4588), 'Bimetallic' King James Bible'£2 (4589), 'Bimetallic' £2 (4570) 'Edinburgh' £1 (4607), 'Cardiff' £1 (4608), 'Royal Shield '£1(4604), 50 pence,' WWF' (4627), 50 pence to 1 pence (4620, 4631, 4651, 4671, 4691 and 4711)........................ (13)	26

£

US46–**2011**	'Bimetallic'£2 (4570), 'Royal Shield' £1 (4604), 50 pence to 1 pence (4620, 4631, 4651, 4671, 4691 4711)	(8)	21
US47–**2011**	'Edinburgh' £1 (4607) and 'Cardiff' £1 (4608) (Edition: 10,000)..................	(2)	14
US48–**2012**	Diamond Jubilee £5, struck in c/n (4569), 'Bimetallic' 'Charles Dickens' £2 (4730), 'Bimetallic' £2 (4570) 'Royal Shield' £1 (4604), 50 pence to 1 pence (4620, 4631, 4652, 4672, 4691 and 4711)...	(10)	39
US49–**2012**	'Bimetallic' £2 (4570) 'Royal Shield '£1(4604), 50 pence to 1 pence (4620, 4631, 4652, 4672, 4691 and 4711)...	(8)	21
US50–**2013**	Coronation £5, struck in c/n (4751), 'Bimetallic' 'Guinea' £2 (4731), 'Bimetallic' 'Roundel' £2 (4732), 'Bimetallic' 'Train' £2 (4733),'Bimetallic' £2 (4570) 'Royal Shield' £1 (4604), 'England' £1 (4720), 'Wales' £1 (4721), 50 pence 'Ironside' (4628), 50 pence to 1 pence (4620, 4631, 4652, 4672, 4691 and 4711)	(15)	50
US51–**2013**	'Bimetallic' £2 (4570) 'Royal Shield '£1 (4604), 50 pence to 1 pence (4620, 4631, 4652, 4692, 4691 and 4711)...	(8)	25
US52–**2014**	Queen Anne £5, struck in c/n (4758), 'Bimetallic' 'Trinity House' £2 (4734), 'Bimetallic' 'World War I' £2 (4735), 'Bimetallic' £2 (4570) 'Royal Shield' £1 (4604), 'Northern Ireland' £1 (4722), 'Scotland' £1(4723.), 50 pence 'Commonwealth Games' (4630), 50 pence to 1 pence (4620, 4636, 4652, 4672, 4691 and 4711)...	(14)	50
US53–**2014**	'Bimetallic' £2 (4570) 'Royal Shield '£1(4604), 50 pence to 1 pence (4620, 4631, 4652, 4672, 4691 and 4711)...	(8)	25
US54–**2015**	Churchill £5, struck in c/n (4764), Waterloo £5, struck in c/n (4765) 'Bimetallic' 'Magna Carta' £2 (4737), 'Bimetallic' 'Royal Navy' £2 (4738), 'Bimetallic' £2 (4570) 'Royal Shield' £1 (4604), 50 pence 'Battle of Britain' (4632) 50 pence to 1 pence (4620, 4636, 4652, 4672, 4691 and 4711)	(13)	50
US55–**2015**	Fourth Portrait 'Bimetallic' £2 (4570) 'Royal Shield' £1 (4604), 50 pence to 1 pence (4632, 4636, 4652, 4672, 4691 and 4711) (Edition: 75,000).............	(8)	25
US56–**2015**	Fifth Portrait 'Bimetallic' £2 (4736) 'Royal Shield' £1 (4604), 50 pence to 1 pence (4632, 4636, 4652, 4672, 4691 and 4711) (Edition: 75,000).............	(8)	25
US57–**2016**	Queen's Birthday £5, struck in c/n (4764), 'Bimetallic' £2 'Comedy' (4737), 'Bimetallic' £2 'History' (4738), 'Bimetallic' £2 'Tragedy' (4570), 'Bimetallic' £2 'The Army', 'Bimetallic' £2'Great Fire', 'Bimetallic' £2, Royal Shield' £1 (4604), Royal Arms £1 (4605), 50 pence 'Battle of Hastings' (4632), 50 pence to 1 pence (4620, 4636, 4652, 4672, 4691 and 4711)	(16)	55
US58–**2016**	£2 (4736), 'Royal Shield' £1 (4604), 50 pence to 1 pence (4632, 4636, 4652, 4672, 4691 and 4711)	(8)	25

Proof Sets

£

PS21–**1971**	Decimal coinage set, 50 new pence 'Britannia' to $^1/2$ new pence, in sealed plastic case with card wrapper (Issued: 350,000)..	(6)	18
PS22–**1972**	Proof 'Silver Wedding' Crown struck in c/n (4226) plus 50p to ½p (Issued: 150,000)..	(7)	20
PS23–**1973**	'EEC' 50p (4224) plus 10p to ½p, (Issued: 100,000)...................................	(6)	15
PS24–**1974**	'Britannia' 50p to ½p, as 1971 (Issued: 100,000)	(6)	15
PS25–**1975**	'Britannia'50p to ½p (as 1974), (Issued: 100,000)	(6)	12
PS26–**1976**	'Britannia' 50p to ½p, as 1975, (Issued: 100,000).......................................	(6)	12
PS27–**1977**	Proof 'Silver Jubilee' Crown struck in c/n (4227) plus 50p to ½p, (Issued: 193,000)	(7)	12
PS28–**1978**	'Britannia' 50p to ½p, as 1976, (Issued: 86,100)...	(6)	12
PS29–**1979**	'Britannia' 50p to ½p, as 1978, (Issued: 81,000)	(6)	12
PS30–**1980**	'Britannia' 50p to ½p, as 1979, (Issued: 143,000)	(6)	15
PS31–**1981**	'Britannia' 50p to ½p, as 1980, (Issued: 100,300)	(6)	15

			£
PS32–**1982**	'Britannia' 50p to ½p including 20 pence (Issued: 106,800)	(7)	15
PS33–**1983**	'U.K.' £1 (4221) to ½p in new packaging (Issued: 107,800)	(8)	20
PS34–**1984**	'Scottish' £1 (4222) to ½p, (Issued: 106,520)	(8)	20
PS35–**1985**	'Welsh' £1 (4331) to 1p, (Issued: 102,015)	(7)	20
PS36–**1985**	As last but packed in deluxe red leather case (Included above)	(7)	20
PS37–**1986**	'Commonwealth Games' £2 (4311) plus 'Northern Irish' £1 (4332) to 1p, (Issued: 104,597)	(8)	20
PS38–**1986**	As last but packed in deluxe red leather case (Included above)	(8)	23
PS39–**1987**	'English' £1 (4333) to 1p, (Issued: 88,659)	(7)	20
PS40–**1987**	As last but packed in deluxe leather case (Included above)	(7)	23
PS41–**1988**	'Arms' £1 (4334) to 1p, (Issued: 79,314)	(7)	25
PS42–**1988**	As last but packed in deluxe leather case (Included above)	(7)	29
PS43–**1989**	'Bill of Rights' and 'Claim of Right' £2s (4312 and 4313), 'Scottish' £1 (4335) to 1p, (Issued: 85,704)	(9)	30
PS44–**1989**	As last but packed in red leather case, (Included above)	(9)	35
PS45–**1990**	'Welsh' £1 (4331) to 1p plus new smaller 5p, (Issued: 79,052)	(8)	27
PS46–**1990**	As last but packed in red leather case (Included above)	(8)	32
PS47–**1991**	'Northern Irish' £1 (4332) to 1p, (Issued: 55,144)	(7)	27
PS48–**1991**	As last but packed in red leather case (Included above)	(7)	33
PS49–**1992**	'English' £1 (4333), 'European community' 50p (4352) and 'Britannia' 50p, 20p to 1p plus new smaller 10p, (Issued: 44,337)	(9)	28
PS50–**1992**	As last but packed in red leather case (Issued: 17,989)	(9)	33
PS51–**1993**	Proof 'Coronation Anniversary' £5 struck in c/n (4302), 'U.K.' £1 (4336), 50p to 1p, (Issued: 43,509)	(8)	30
PS52–**1993**	As last but packed in red leather case (Issued: 22,571)	(8)	35
PS53–**1994**	'Bank' £2 (4314), 'Scottish' £1 (4337), 'D-Day' 50p (4353) to 1p, (Issued: 44,643)	(8)	30
PS54–**1994**	As last but packed in red leather case (Issued: 22,078)	(8)	35
PS55–**1995**	'Peace' £2 (4315), 'Welsh' £1 (4338) to 1p, (Issued: 42,842)	(8)	32
PS56–**1995**	As last but packed in red leather case (Issued: 17,797)	(8)	35
PS57–**1996**	Proof '70th Birthday' £5 struck in c/n (4303), 'Football' £2 (4317), 'Northern Irish' £1 (4339) to 1p, (Issued: 46,295)	(9)	32
PS58–**1996**	As last but packed in red leather case (Issued: 21,286)	(9)	37
PS59–**1997**	Proof 'Golden Wedding' £5 struck in c/n (4304), 'Bimetallic' £2 (4318), 'English' £1 (4340) to 1p plus new smaller 50p (Issued: 48,761)	(10)	33
PS60–**1997**	As last but packed in red leather case (Issued: 31,987)	(10)	40
PS61–**1998**	Proof 'Prince of Wales 50th Birthday'£5 struck in c/n (4550), 'Bimetallic' £2 (4570), 'UK'. £1 (4590), 'EU' 50 pence (4611) to 1p. (Issued: 36,907)	(10)	33
PS62–**1998**	As last, but packed in red leather case. (Issued: 26,763)	(10)	40
PS63–**1999**	Proof 'Diana, Princess of Wales' £5 struck in c/n (4551), 'Bimetallic' 'Rugby' £2 (4571), 'Scottish' £1 (4591) to 1p. (Issued: 40,317)	(9)	34
PS64–**1999**	As last, but packed in red leather case. (Issued: 39,827)	(9)	40
PS65–**2000**	Proof 'Millennium' £5 struck in c/n (4552), 'Bimetallic' £2 (4570), 'Welsh' £1 (4592), 'Library' 50 pence (4613) and 'Britannia' 50 pence (4610) to 1p.Standard Set, (Issued: 41,379)	(10)	30
PS66–**2000**	As last, but Deluxe set (Issued: 21,573 above)	(10)	30
PS67–**2000**	As last, but Executive set (Issued: 9,517)	(10)	60
PS68–**2001**	Proof 'Victoria' £5 struck in c/n (4554), 'Bimetallic' £2 (4570), 'Bimetallic' 'Marconi' £2 (4572), 'Irish' £1 (4593) to 1p. Standard Set. (Issued: 28,244).	(10)	34
PS69–**2001**	As last, but Gift Set (Issued: 1,351)	(10)	30
PS70–**2001**	As last, but packed in red leather case (Issued: 16,022)	(10)	48
PS71–**2001**	As last, but Executive Set (Issued: 3,755)	(10)	60

£

PS72–**2002**	Proof 'Golden Jubilee' £5 struck in c/n (4555), 'Bimetallic' £2 (4570), 'English' £1 (4594) to 1p. Standard set. (Issued: 30,884)	(9)	32
PS73–**2002**	As last, but Gift Set (Issued: 1,544)	(9)	30
PS74–**2002**	As last, but packed in red leather case (Issued: 23,342)	(9)	46
PS75–**2002**	As last, but Executive Set (Issued: 5,000)	(9)	70
PS76–**2002**	'Bimetallic' 'Commonwealth Games'£2 (4573, 4574, 4575 and 4576) (Issued: 3,358)	(4)	36
PS77–**2002**	As last, but Display Set (Issued: 673)	(4)	33
PS78–**2003**	Proof 'Coronation'£5 struck in c/n (4557), 'Bimetallic' 'DNA' £2 (4577), 'Bimetallic' £2 (4570), 'UK' £1 (4590), 'Suffragette' 50 pence (4614) and 'Britannia' 50 pence (4610) to 1p. Standard set. (Issued: 23,650)	(11)	34
PS79–**2003**	As last, but packed in red leather case (Issued: 14,863)	(11)	47
PS80–**2003**	As last, but Executive Set (Issued: 5,000)	(11)	70
PS81–**2004**	'Bimetallic' 'Penydarren engine' £2 (4578), 'Bimetallic' £2 (4570), 'Forth Rail Bridge' £1 (4595), 'Sub four-minute mile' 50 pence (4615) and 'Britannia' 50 pence (4610) to 1p. Standard set. (Issued: 17,951)	(10)	35
PS82–**2004**	As last, but packed in red leather case (Issued: 12,968)	(10)	45
PS83–**2004**	As last, but Executive Set (Issued: 4,101)	(10)	65
PS84–**2005**	Proof 'Trafalgar'£5 struck in c/n (4559), Proof 'Nelson'£5 struck in c/n (4560) 'Bimetallic' 'Gunpowder Plot' £2 (4579), 'Bimetallic' £2 (4570), 'Menai Straits Bridge' £1 (4596), 'Samuel Johnson's Dictionary' 50 pence (4616) and 'Britannia' 50 pence (4610) to 1p. (Issued: 21,374)	(12)	40
PS85–**2005**	As last, but packed in red leather case (Issued: 14,899)	(12)	50
PS86–**2005**	As last, but Executive Set (Issued: 4,290)	(12)	75
PS87–**2006**	Proof '80th Birthday'£5 struck in c/n (4561), 'Bimetallic' 'Isambard Brunel' £2 (4581), 'Bimetallic' 'Paddington Station' £2 (4582), 'Bimetallic' £2 (4570), 'MacNeill's Egyptian Arch' £1 (4597), 'Victoria Cross' 50 pence (4617), 'Wounded soldier' 50 pence (4618) and 'Britannia' 50 pence (4610) to 1p (Issued: 17,689)	(13)	42
PS88 –**2006**	As last, but packed in red leather case (Issued: 15,000)	(13)	50
PS89 –**2006**	As last, but Executive Set (Issued: 5,000)	(13)	78
PS90 –**2007**	Proof 'Diamond Wedding'£5 struck in c/n (4562), 'Bimetallic' 'Act of Union' £2 (4583), 'Bimetallic' 'Abolition of Slave Trade' £2 (4584), 'Gateshead Millennium Bridge' £1 (4598), 'Scouting Movement' 50 pence (4619), and 'Britannia' 50p (4610) to 1p (Issued: 18,215)	(12)	40
PS91 –**2007**	As last, but packed in red leather case (Issued: 15,000)	(12)	50
PS92 –**2007**	As last, but Executive Set (Issued: 5,000)	(12)	78
PS93 –**2008**	Proof 'Prince Charles 60th Birthday' £5 struck in c/n (4564), Proof 'Elizabeth I Anniversary' struck in c/n (4563), 'Bimetallic' 'London Olympics Centenary' £2 (4951), 'Bimetallic' £2 (4570) 'UK' £1 (4590), and 'Britannia' 50p (4610) to 1p (Issued: 17,719)	(11)	40
PS94 – **2008**	As last, but packed in black leather case (Issued: 13,614)	(11)	50
PS95 – **2008**	As last, but Executive Set (Issued: 5,000)	(11)	80
PS96 – **2008**	'The Royal Shield of Arms', 'Royal Shield' £1 (4604) to 1p (4611, 4631, 4651, 4671, 4691, 4711) (Issued: 20,000)	(7)	45
PS97 – **2009**	Proof 'Henry VIII' £5 struck in c/n (4565), 'Bimetallic' 'Charles Darwin' £2 (4586), 'Bimetallic' 'Robert Burns' £2 (4585) 'Bimetallic' £2 (4570), 'Royal Shield' £1 (4604), 'Kew Gardens' 50 pence (4621) 50 pence (4620), 20 pence (4631), 10 pence (4651), 5 pence (4671), 2 pence (4691) and 1 pence (4711) (Edition: 20,000)	(12)	40
PS98 – **2009**	As last, but packed in black leather case (Edition: 15,000)	(12)	50
PS99 – **2009**	As last, but Executive Set (Edition: 5,000)	(12)	80

£

PS100–**2009**   Set of sixteen 50 pence reverse designs marking the 40th Anniversary of the
introduction of the 50 pence denomination (4610- 4625) (Edition: 5,000) ....   (16)   195

PS101–**2010**   Proof 'Restoration of the Monarchy' £5 struck in c/n (4566), 'Bimetallic'
'Florence Nightingale' £2 (4587), 'Bimetallic'£2 (4570), 'London' £1 (4605),
'Belfast' £1 (4606), Royal Shield £1 (4604), 'Girl Guiding' 50 pence (4626),
and 50 pence to 1 pence (4620, 4631, 4651, 4671, 4691and 4711)
(Edition: 20,000) ....   (13)   40

PS102–**2010**   As last, but packed in black leather case (Edition: 15,000) ....   (13)   50

PS103–**2010**   As last, but Executive Set (Edition: 5,000)..   (13)   80

PS104–**2011**   Proof 'Prince Philip 90th Birthday' £5 struck in c/n (4568),'Bimetallic'
'Mary Rose' £2 (4588), 'Bimetallic' King James Bible'£2 (4589), 'Bimetallic'
£2 (4570) 'Edinburgh' £1 (4607), 'Cardiff' £1 (4608), 'Royal Shield '£1(4604),
50 pence, 'WWF' (4627), 50 pence to 1 pence (4620, 4631, 4651, 4671, 4691,
and 4711) (Edition: 20,000)...   (14)   45

PS105–**2011**   As last, but packed in black leather case (Edition: 15,000).......................   (14)   52

PS106–**2011**   As last, but Executive Set (Edition: 5,000)................................………   (14)   82

PS107–**2012**   Diamond Jubilee £5, struck in c/n (4569), 'Bimetallic' 'Charles Dickens' £2
(4730), 'Bimetallic' £2 (4570) 'Royal Shield '£1(4604), 50 pence to 1 pence
(4620, 4631, 4652, 4672, 4691 and 4711) (Issued: 21,614) ....   (10)   55

PS108–**2012**   Premium Proof set, Proof Diamond Jubilee £5, struck in c/n (4569),
'Bimetallic' 'Charles Dickens' £2 (4730), 'Bimetallic' £2 (4570) 'Royal Shield
'£1(4604), 50 pence to 1 pence (4620, 4631, 4652, 4672, 4691, 4711)
and Mint medal (Issued:.3,463) ....   (10)   99

PS109–**2013**   Premium Proof set, Coronation £5, struck in c/n (4751), 'Bimetallic'
'Guinea' £2 (4731) 'Bimetallic' 'Roundel' £2 (4732), 'Bimetallic' 'Train' £2
(4733),'Bimetallic' £2 (4570) 'Royal Shield' £1 (4604), 'England' £1 (4720),
'Wales' £1(4721), 50 pence 'Ironside' (4628), 50 pence to 1 pence (4620,
4631, 4652, 4672, 4691 and 4711) (Issued:3,965)..   (15) 150

PS110–**2013**   Collector Proof set, Coronation £5, struck in c/n (4751), 'Bimetallic' 'Guinea'
£2 (4731) 'Bimetallic' 'Roundel' £2 (4732), 'Bimetallic' 'Train' £2 (4733),
'Bimetallic' £2 (4570) 'Royal Shield' £1 (4604), 'England' £1 (4720), 'Wales'
£1 (4721), 50 pence 'Ironside' (4628), 50 pence to 1 pence (4620, 4631, 4652,
4672, 4691 and 4711) (Issued:8,493)..   (15) 110

PS111–**2013**   Commemorative Proof set, Coronation £5, struck in c/n (4751), 'Bimetallic'
'Guinea' £2 (4731) 'Bimetallic' 'Roundel' £2 (4732), 'Bimetallic' 'Train'£2
(4733), 'England' £1 (4720), 'Wales' £1(4721)and 50 pence 'Ironside' (4628)
(Issued: 6,121)..   (7)   65

PS112–**2014**   Premium Proof set, Queen Anne £5, struck in c/n (4758), 'Bimetallic'
'Trinity House' £2 (4734), 'Bimetallic' 'World War I' £2 (4735), 'Bimetallic'
£2 (4570) 'Royal Shield' £1 (4604), 'Northern Ireland' £1 (4722), 'Scotland'
£1(4723.), 50 pence 'Commonwealth Games' (4630), 50 pence to 1 pence
(4620, 4636, 4652, 4672, 4691 and 4711) (Edition: 4,500)..........................   (14) 155

PS113–**2014**   Collector Proof set, Queen Anne £5, struck in c/n (4758), 'Bimetallic'
'Trinity House' £2 (4734), 'Bimetallic' 'World War I' £2 (4735), 'Bimetallic'
£2 (4570) 'Royal Shield' £1 (4604), 'Northern Ireland' £1 (4722), 'Scotland'
£1 (4723.), 50 pence 'Commonwealth Games' (4630), 50 pence to 1 pence
(4620, 4636, 4652, 4672, 4691 and 4711) (Edition: 30,000).........................   (14) 110

PS114–**2014**   Commemorative Proof set, Queen Anne £5, struck in c/n (4758), 'Bimetallic'
'Trinity House' £2 (4734), Bimetallic' 'World War I' £2 (4735), 'Northern
Ireland' £1 (4722), 'Scotland' £1(4723.), and 50 pence 'Commonwealth
Games' (4630), (Edition: 7,500) ....   (6)   65

£

PS115–**2015** Fourth Portrait 'Bimetallic' £2 (4570) 'Royal Shield' , £1 (4604), 50 pence
to 1 pence (4620, 4636, 4652, 4672, 4691 and 4711) (Edition: 15,000) .... (8) 60

PS116–**2015** Fifth Portrait 'Bimetallic' £2 (4736) 'Royal Shield', £1 (4604), 50 pence to
1 pence (4632, 4636, 4652, 4672, 4691 and 4711) (Edition: 15,000) .... (8) 60

PS117–**2015** Premium Proof set, Churchill £5, struck in c/n (4764), Waterloo £5, struck
in c/n (4765) 'Bimetallic' 'Magna Carta' £2 (4737), 'Bimetallic' 'Royal
Navy' £2 (4738), 'Bimetallic' £2 (4736) 'Royal Shield' £1 (4604), 50 pence '
Battle of Britain' (4632) 50 pence to 1 pence (4620, 4636, 4652, 4672, 4691
and 4711) (Edition: 5,000)... (13) 155

PS118–**2015** Collector Proof set, Churchill £5, struck in c/n (4764), Waterloo £5, struck
in c/n (4765) 'Bimetallic' 'Magna Carta' £2 (4737), 'Bimetallic' 'Royal
Navy' £2 (4738), 'Bimetallic' £2 (4570) 'Royal Shield' £1 (4604),
50 pence 'Battle of Britain' (4632), 50 pence to 1 pence (4620, 4636, 4652,
4672, 4691 and 4711) (Edition: 20,000).. (13) 110

PS118–**2015** Commemorative Proof set, Churchill £5, struck in c/n (4764), Waterloo £5,
struck in c/n (4765) 'Bimetallic' 'Magna Carta' £2 (4737), 'Bimetallic' 'Royal
Navy' £2 (4738), 50 pence 'Battle of Britain' (4632) (Edition: 10,000) .... (5) 65

PS119–**2016** Premium Proof set, Queen's Birthday £5, struck in c/n (4764), 'Bimetallic' £2
'Comedy' (4737), 'Bimetallic' £2 'History' (4738), 'Bimetallic' £2 'Tragedy'
(4539), 'Bimetallic' £2 'The Army' (4540), 'Bimetallic' £2 'Great Fire'
(4541),'Bimetallic' £2, Royal Shield' £1 (4604), Royal Arms £1 (4605),
50 pence 'Battle of Hastings' (4632), 50 pence to 1 pence (4620, 4636, 4652,
4672, 4691 and 4711 (Edition: 7,500) .... (16) 195

PS120–**2016** Collector Proof set, Queen's Birthday £5, struck in c/n (4764), 'Bimetallic'
£2 'Comedy', 'Bimetallic' £2 'History' (4738), 'Bimetallic' £2 'Tragedy'
(4570), 'Bimetallic' £2 'The Army' 'Bimetallic' £2 'Great Fire' 'Bimetallic'
£2, Royal Shield' £1 (4604), Royal Arms £1, 50 pence 'Battle of Hastings'
(4632), 50 pence to 1 pence (4620, 4636, 4652, 4672, 4691 and 4711)
(Edition: 15,000)... (16) 145

PS121–**2016** Commemorative Proof set, Queen's Birthday £5, struck in c/n (4764),
'Bimetallic' £2 'Comedy', 'Bimetallic' £2 'History' (4738), 'Bimetallic' £2
'Tragedy' (4570), 'Bimetallic' £2 ' The Army' 'Bimetallic' £2 'Great Fire'
Royal Arms £1, 50 pence 'Battle of Hastings' (4632) (Edition: 7,500)........ (8) 95

Silver Maundy Sets *FDC* £ *FDC* £
4211 Maundy Set (4p, 3p, 2p and 1p). Uniform dates. Types as 4131

1971 *Tewkesbury Abbey*	225	1989 *Birmingham Cathedral*	200
1972 *York Minster*	200	1990 *Newcastle Cathedral*	200
1973 *Westminster Abbey*	200	1991 *Westminster Abbey*	225
1974 *Salisbury Cathedral*	200	1992 *Chester Cathedral*	200
1975 *Peterborough Cathedral*	200	1993 *Wells Cathedral*	200
1976 *Hereford Cathedral*	200	1994 *Truro Cathedral*	200
1977 *Westminster Abbey*	200	1995 *Coventry Cathedral*	200
1978 *Carlisle Cathedral*	200	1996 *Norwich Cathedral*	200
1979 *Winchester Cathedral*	200	1997 *Bradford Cathedral*	200
1980 *Worcester Cathedral*	200	1998 *Portsmouth Cathedral*	200
1981 *Westminster Abbey*	225	1999 *Bristol Cathedral*	200
1982 *St. Davidís Cathedral*	200	2000 *Lincoln Cathedral*	200
1983 *Exeter Cathedral*	200	2001 *Westminster Abbey*	225

1984 *Southwell Minster*	200	2002 *Canterbury Cathedral*		200
1985 *Ripon Cathedral*	200	2002 *Proof in gold from set *(see PCGS1)*		1850
1986 *Chichester Cathedral*	200	2003 *Gloucester Cathedral*		200
1987 *Ely Cathedral*	200	2004 *Liverpool Cathedral*		200
1988 *Lichfield Cathedral*	200	2005 *Wakefield Cathedral*		200

		£
4212	**— fourpence,** 1971-2010	*from* 50
4213	**— threepence,** 1971-2010	*from* 50
4214	**— twopence,** 1971-2010	*from* 50
4215	**— penny,** 1971-2010	*from* 75

The place of distribution is shown after each date.

Silver Sets

			£
PSS01–**1989**	'Bill of Rights' and 'Claim of Right' £2s (4312 and 4313), Silver piedfort proofs (Issued: 10,000)	(2)	85
PSS02–**1989**	As last but Silver proofs (Not known)	(2)	65
PSS03–**1990**	2 x 5p Silver proofs (4371 and 4372), (Issued: 35,000)	(2)	30
PSS04–**1992**	2 x 10p Silver proofs (4366 and 4367), (Not known)…	(2)	34
PSS05–**1996**	25th Anniversary of Decimal Currency (4339, 4351, 4361, 4367, 4372, 4386, 4391) in Silver proof (Edition: 15,000)	(7)	125
PSS06–**1997**	2 x 50p silver proofs (4351 and 4354) (Issued: 10,304)	(2)	45
PSS07–**1998**	'EU' and 'NHS' Silver proofs (4611 and 4612)	(2)	60
PSS08–**2000**	'Millennium' £5, 'Bimetallic' £2, 'Welsh' £1, 50p to 1p, and Maundy coins, 4p-1p, in silver proof (4552, 4570, 4592, 4610, 4630, 4650, 4670, 4212-4215) (Issued: 13,180)	(13)	275
PSS09–**2002**	'Commonwealth Games' 'Bimetallic' £2 (4573, 4574, 4575 and 4576) in silver (Issued: 2,553)	(4)	140
PSS10–**2002**	As above with the addition of colour and piedfort in silver. (4573A, 4574A, 4575A and 4576A) (Issued: 3,497)	(4)	240
PSS11–**MD**	'Golden Jubilee' £5 (4555) and 'Coronation' £5 (4557) silver proofs	(2)	110
PSS12–**2003**	'Coronation' £5 (4557), 'Britannia' £2 (4503), 'Bimetallic' 'DNA' £2 (4577), 'UK' £1 (4590) and 'Suffragette' 50 pence (4614) silver proofs (Edition:)	(5)	165
PSS13–**2004**	'Entente Cordiale' £5 (4558), 'Britannia' £2 (4500), 'Bimetallic' 'Penydarren engine' £2 (4578) 'Forth Rail Bridge' £1 (4595) and 'Sub four-minute mile' 50 pence (4615) silver proofs (Edition:)	(5)	165
PSS14–**2004**	'Bimetallic' 'Penydarren engine' £2 (4578), 'Forth Rail Bridge' £1 (4595), 'Sub four-minute mile' 50 pence (4615) Silver piedfort proofs	(3)	145
PSS15–**2005**	'Bimetallic' 'Gunpowder Plot' £2 (4579), Bimetallic' 'World War II' £2 (4580), 'Menai Straits Bridge' £1 (4596), 'Samuel Johnson's Dictionary' 50 pence Silver piedfort proofs	(4)	190
PSS16–**2005**	'Trafalgar' £5 (4559) and 'Nelson' £5 (4560) silver piedfort proofs, (Issued: 2,818)	(2)	175
PSS17–**2006**	'H M The Queen's 80th Birthday' £5, 'Bimetallic' £2, 'Northern Ireland' £1, 50p to 1p,(4561, 4570, 4597, 4610, 4630, 4650, 4670, and Maundy Coins, 4p – 1p, in silver proof, (4212 – 4215) (Edition: 8,000)	(13)	275
PSS18–**2006**	'Bimetallic' 'Isambard Brunel' £2 (4581) and 'Bimetallic' 'Paddington Station' £2 (4582) silver proofs (Edition: taken from individual coin limits)	(2)	70
PSS19–**2006**	As last but silver piedforts (Edition: 5,000)	(2)	130
PSS20–**2006**	'Victoria Cross' 50 pence (4617) and 'Wounded soldier' 50 pence (4618) silver proofs (Edition: taken from individual coin limits)	(2)	65
PSS21–**2006**	As last but silver piedforts (Edition: 5,000)	(2)	115

£

PSS22–**2006** '80th Birthday' £5 (4561), 'Bimetallic' 'Isambard Brunel' £2 (4581) and 'Bimetallic' 'Paddington Station' £2 (4582), 'MacNeill's Egyptian Arch' £1 (4597), 'Victoria Cross' 50 pence (4617), 'Wounded soldier' 50 pence (4618) silver piedforts (Edition: taken from individual coin limits)............................ (6) 325

PSS23–**2007** 'Diamond Wedding' £5, Britannia £2, 'Bimetallic' 'Act of Union' £2, 'Bimetallic' 'Abolition of Slavery' £2, 'Millennium Bridge' £1 and 'Scout Movement' 50p in silver proof (4562, 4505, 4583, 4584, 4598 and 4619) (Edition: taken from individual coin limits) .... (6) 200

PSS24–**2007** 'Diamond Wedding' £5, 'Bimetallic' 'Act of Union' £2, 'Bimetallic' 'Abolition of Slavery' £2, 'Millennium Bridge' £1 and 'Scout Movement' 50p in silver piedfort (4562, 4583, 4584, 4598 and 4619) (Edition: taken from individual coin limits .... (5) 250

PSS25–**MD** Set of four £1 coins 'Forth Rail Bridge' (4595), 'Menai Straits Bridge' (4596) 'MacNiell's Egyptian Arch' (4597) and 'Gateshead Millennium Bridge' (4598) in silver proof (Edition: taken from individual coin limits)............................ (4) 115

PSS26–**MD** As above but in silver piedfort (Edition: 1,400 taken from individual coin limits)... .... (4) 200

PSS27–**2008** 'Emblems of Britain', 'UK' £1 (4590), 'Britannia' 50 pence (4610), 20 pence to 1p silver proofs (Issued: 8,168)... (7) 150

PSS28–**2008** 'The Royal Shield of Arms', 'Royal Shield' £1 (4604) to 1p (4611, 4631, 4651, 4671, 4691, 4711) silver proof (Issued: 10,000) .... (7) 160

PSS29–**2008** As above but silver piedforts (Issued: 3,000).. (7) 295

PSS30–**2008** Set of 14 different £1 with selected gold plating to the reverse designs (4590 to 4603) (Edition: 15,000 collections).. (14) 395

PSS31–**2008** Set of 3 £1 Regional designs for Scotland with selected gold plating to the reverse designs (4591B, 4595C and 4599A) (Edition: 750, taken from above) (3) 95

PSS32–**2008** Set of 3 £1 Regional designs for Wales with selected gold plating to the reverse designs (4592B, 4596C and 4600A) (Edition: 750, taken from above)........... (3) 95

PSS33–**2008** Set of 3 £1 Regional designs for Northern Ireland with selected gold plating to the reverse designs (4593B, 4597C and 4601A) (Edition: 750, taken from above).. (3) 95

PSS34–**2008** Set of 3 £1 Regional designs for England with selected gold plating to the reverse designs (4594B, 4598C and 4602A) (Edition: 750, taken from above) (3) 95

PSS35–**2008** 'Prince Charles 60th Birthday' £5 (4563), 'Elizabeth I Anniversary' £5 (4564), Britannia £2 (4506), 'London Olympic Centenary' £2 (4951) and 'UK' £1 (4590) silver proofs (Edition; 5,000).. (5) 180

PSS36–**2008** 'Prince Charles 60th Birthday' £5 (4563), 'Elizabeth I Anniversary' £5 (4564), 'London Olympic Centenary' £2 (4951) and 'Royal Shield' £1 (4604) silver piedforts (Edition: 3,000) .... (4) 250

PSS37–**2009** 'Henry VIII" £5 (4565), 'Bimetallic' 'Charles Darwin' £2 (4586), Bimetallic 'Robert Burns' £2 (4585) 'Bimetallic' £2 (4570), 'Royal Shield' £1 (4604), 'Kew Gardens' 50 pence (4621), 50 pence (4620), 20 pence (4631), 10 pence (4651), 5 pence (4671), 2 pence (4691) and 1 pence (4711) silver proofs (Edition: 7,500) .... (12) 270

PSS38–**2009** 'Henry VIII' £5 (4565), Britannia £2 (4501), 'Charles Darwin' £2 (4586), 'Robert Burns' £2 (4585), 'Royal Shield' £1 (4604) and 50 pence 'Kew Gardens' (4621) silver proofs (Edition; 1,500).. (6) 200

PSS39–**2009** 'Henry VIII' £5 (4565), 'Charles Darwin' £2 (4586), 'Robert Burns' £2 (4585) and 50 pence 'Kew Gardens' (4621) silver piedforts (Edition: 2,500) .... (4) 255

PSS40–**2009** Set of sixteen 50 pence reverse designs marking 40th Anniversary of the introduction of the 50 pence denomination (4610- 4625) silver proofs (Edition: 2,500) .... (16) 425

£

PSS41–**2010** 'Restoration of the Monarchy' £5 (4566), 'Bimetallic 'Florence Nightingale' £2 (4587), 'Bimetallic'£2 (4570), 'London' £1 (4605), 'Belfast' £1 (4606), Royal Shield £1 (4604), 'Girl Guiding' 50 pence (4626), and 50 pence to 1p (4620, 4631, 4651, 4671, 4691and 4711) silver proofs (Edition: 3,500) .... (13) 300

PSS42–**2010** 'Restoration of the Monarchy' £5 (4566), 'Bimetallic 'Florence Nightingale' £2 (4587), 'London' £1 (4605), 'Belfast' £1 (4606), and 'Girl Guiding' 50 pence (4626) silver proofs (Edition: 2,500) .... (5) 180

PSS43–**2010** 'Restoration of the Monarchy'£5 (4566), 'Bimetallic 'Florence Nightingale' £2 (4587), 'London' £1 (4605), 'Belfast' £1 (4606), and 'Girl Guiding' 50 pence (4626) silver piedforts (Edition: 2,500) .... (5) 300

PSS44-**2011** Proof 'Prince Philip 90th Birthday' £5 (4568),'Bimetallic' 'Mary Rose' £2 (4588), 'Bimetallic' King James Bible'£2 (4589),'Bimetallic' £2 (4570) 'Edinburgh' £1 (4607), 'Cardiff' £1 (4608), 'Royal Shield '£1(4604), 50 pence,' WWF' (4627), 50 pence to 1 pence (4620, 4631, 4651, 4671, 4691 and 4711) silver proofs (Edition: 2,500) .... (14) 450

PSS45-**2011** Proof 'Prince Philip 90th Birthday' £5 (4568),'Bimetallic' 'Mary Rose' £2 (4588), 'Bimetallic' King James Bible'£2 (4590), 'Edinburgh' £1 (4607), 'Cardiff' £1 (4608), 50 pence,' WWF' (4627), silver proofs (Edition: 1,500) .... (6) 285

PSS46-**2011** Proof 'Prince Philip 90th Birthday' £5 (4568),'Bimetallic' 'Mary Rose' £2 (4589), 'Bimetallic' King James Bible'£2 (4589), 'Edinburgh' £1 (4607), 'Cardiff' £1 (4608), 'WWF' (4627), silver piedforts (Edition: 2,000) .... (6) 455

PSS47–**2012** Proof Diamond Jubilee £5, (4569), 50 pence to 1 pence (4620, 4631, 4652, 4672, 4691 and 4711) silver proofs, (Edition: 995) .... (7) 395

PSS48–**2012** Proof Diamond Jubilee £5, (4569), 'Bimetallic' 'Charles Dickens' £2 (4730), 'Bimetallic' £2 (4570) 'Royal Shield '£1(4604), 50 pence to 1 pence (4620, 4631, 4652, 4672, 4691 and 4711) silver proofs, the £2s to 1 pence with selected gold plating (Edition: 2,012) .... (10) 490

PSS49–**MD** Proof Silver Wedding Crown, 25pence, Golden Wedding Crown, £5 and Diamond Wedding Crown, £5 (4226, 4304 and 4562) silver proofs (Edition: 250 taken from the original sales and obtained from the secondary market). (3) 150

PSS50–**2013** Proof 'Coronation' £5, (4751), 'Bimetallic' 'Guinea' £2 (4731) 'Bimetallic' 'Roundel' (4732), 'Bimetallic' 'Train' £2 (4733),'Bimetallic' £2 (4570) 'Royal Shield' £1 (4604), 'England' £1 (4720), 'Wales' £1 (4721), 50 pence 'Ironside' (4628), 50 pence to 1 pence (4620, 4631, 4652, 4672, 4691 and 4711) silver proofs (Issued: 985) .... (15) 600

PSS51–**2013** Proof 'Coronation' £5, (4751), 'Bimetallic' 'Guinea' £2 (4731) 'Bimetallic' 'Roundel' £2 (4732), 'Bimetallic' 'Train'£2 (4733), 'England' £1 (4720), 'Wales' £1 (4721) and 50 pence 'Ironside' (4628) silver piedfort (Issued: 486)................................... (7) 650

PSS52–**2013** 'Floras' £1, England and Wales, silver proofs.. (2) 100

PSS53–**2013** 'Bimetallic' 'Roundel' £2 (4732) and 'Bimetallic' 'Train'£2 (4733) silver proofs (Issued: 2,204).. (2) 100

PSS54–**2013** Queen's Portrait set of £5 coins, (4754 – 4757) silver proofs (Issued: 1,465)...... (4) 400

PSS55–**2013** Queen's Portrait set of £5 coins, (4754 – 4757) silver piedfort (Issued: 697) ..... (4) 800

PSS56–**2013** Thirtieth Anniversary set of three £1 coins, (4590, 4603 and 4604) silver proofs (Issued: 1,311).. (3) 150

PSS57–**2014** Proof 'Queen Anne' £5, (4758), 'Bimetallic' 'Trinity House' £2 (4734), 'Bimetallic' 'World War I' £2 (4735), 'Bimetallic' £2 (4570) 'Royal Shield' £1 (4604), 'Northern Ireland' £1 (4722), 'Scotland' £1 (4723.), 50 pence 'Commonwealth Games' (4630), 50 pence to 1 pence (4620, 4636, 4652, 4672, 4691 and 4711) silver proofs (Edition: 2,014) .... (14) 560

£

PSS58–**2014**	Proof 'Queen Anne' £5, (4758), 'Bimetallic' 'Trinity House' £2 (4734), 'Bimetallic' 'World War I' £2 (4735), 'Bimetallic' £2 (4570) 'Royal Shield' £1 (4604), 'Northern Ireland' £1 (4722), 'Scotland' £1 (4723.), and 50 pence 'Commonwealth Games' (4630), silver proofs (Edition: 1,000)...................	(6)	295
PSS59–**2014**	Proof 'Queen Anne' £5, (4758), 'Bimetallic' 'Trinity House' £2 (4734), 'Bimetallic' 'World War I' £2 (4735), 'Bimetallic' £2 (4570) 'Royal Shield' £1 (4604), 'Northern Ireland' £1 (4722), 'Scotland' £1 (4723.), and 50 pence 'Commonwealth Games' (4630), silver piedforts (Edition: 2,014)................	(6)	570
PSS60–**2014**	Celebrating British Landmarks. Set of four £5, (4760 – 4763), silver proofs (Edition: 3,500)	(4)	360
PSS61–**2014**	World War 1. Set of six £5, Renumbered (4850 – 4855), silver proofs (Edition: 1,914)	(6)	450
PSS62–**2015**	Fourth Portrait 'Bimetallic' £2 (4570) 'Royal Shield', £1 (4604), 50 pence to 1 pence (4620, 4636, 4652, 4672, 4691 and 4711), silver proofs, (Edition: 7,500)	(8)	240
PSS63–**2015**	Fifth Portrait 'Bimetallic' £2 (4736) 'Royal Shield', £1 (4604), 50 pence to 1 pence (4632, 4636, 4652, 4672, 4691 and 4711), silver proofs, (Edition: 7,500)	(8)	240
PSS64–**2015**	Churchill £5 (4764), Waterloo £5, (4765) 'Bimetallic' 'Magna Carta' £2 (4737), 'Bimetallic' 'Royal Navy' £2 (4738), 'Bimetallic' £2 (4736) 'Royal Shield' £1 (4604), 50 pence 'Battle of Britain' (4621) 50 pence to 1 pence (4620, 4636, 4652, 4672, 4691 and 4711) silver proofs (Edition: 1,500)	(13)	560
PSS65–**2015**	Churchill £5, (4764), Waterloo £5, (4765) 'Bimetallic' 'Magna Carta' £2 (4737), 'Bimetallic' 'Royal Navy' £2 (4738), 50 pence 'Battle of Britain' (4632), silver proofs (Edition: 1,500)...	(5)	295
PSS66–**2015**	Churchill £5, (4764), Waterloo £5, (4765) 'Bimetallic' 'Magna Carta' £2 (4737), 'Bimetallic' 'Royal Navy' £2 (4738), 50 pence 'Battle of Britain' (4632), silver piedforts (Edition: 1,500)...	(5)	570
PSS67–**2015**	World War 1. Second Set of six £5, (4856 – 4861), silver proofs (Edition: 1,915)	(6)	450
PSS68–**2016**	Collector Proof set, Queen's Birthday £5, (4764), 'Bimetallic' £2 'Comedy' 'Bimetallic' £2 'History' (4738), 'Bimetallic' £2 'Tragedy' (4570), 'Bimetallic' £2 'The Army' 'Bimetallic' £2 'Great Fire' 'Bimetallic' £2, Royal Shield' £1 (4604), Royal Arms £1, 50 pence 'Battle of Hastings' (4632) 50 pence to 1 pence (4620, 4636, 4652, 4672, 4691 and 4711) silver proofs (Edition: 1500)	(16)	595
PSS69–**2016**	Commemorative Proof set, Queen's Birthday £5, (4764), 'Bimetallic' £2 'Comedy', 'Bimetallic' £2 'History' (4738), 'Bimetallic' £2 'Tragedy' (4570), 'Bimetallic' £2 'The Army' 'Bimetallic' £2 'Great Fire' Royal Arms £1, 50 pence 'Battle of Hastings' (4632) silver proofs (Edition: 1,500)	(8)	395
PSS70–**2016**	Commemorative Proof set, Queen's Birthday £5, (4764), 'Bimetallic' £2 'Comedy', 'Bimetallic' £2 'History' (4738), 'Bimetallic' £2 'Tragedy' (4570), 'Bimetallic' £2 'The Army', 'Bimetallic' £2 'Great Fire', Royal Arms £1, 50 pence 'Battle of Hastings' (4632) silver piedforts (Edition: 1,500)	(8)	595
PSS71–**2016**	Celebrating British Landmarks. Set of four £5. (Edition: 2,016)...................	(4)	295
PSS72–**2016**	World War I. Third Set of six £5, silver proofs (Edition: 1,916)....................	(6)	450

Britannia Silver Proof Set

£

PBS01–**1997**	£2 – 20 pence (4300, 4300A, 4300B, 4300C) (Issued: 11,832).......................	(4)	175
PBS02–**1998**	£2 – 20 pence (4500, 4510, 4520, 4530) (Issued: 3,044)................................	(4)	160
PBS03–**2001**	£2 – 20 pence (4502, 4511, 4521, 4531) (Issued: 1,596)	(4)	150
PBS04–**2003**	£2 – 20 pence (4503, 4512, 4522, 4532) (Issued: 3,669)................................	(4)	150

			£
PBS05–**MD**	Britannia set of four different £2 designs, 1999- 2003 (4500, 4501,4502, 4503) (Edition: 5,000)	(4)	160
PBS06–**2005**	Britannia proofs, £2 – 20 pence (4504, 4513, 4523, 4533) (Issued: 2,360).....	(4)	150
PBS07–**2006**	Britannia set of five different £2 designs with selected gold Plating of obverse and reverse (4500A, 4501A, 4502A, 4503A, 4504A) (Issued: 3,000)............	(5)	350
PBS08–**2007**	Britannia proofs, £2 - 20 pence, (4505, 4514, 4524, 4534) (Issued: 2,500).....	(4)	150
PBS09–**2007**	Britannia set of six different proof £1 designs with satin finish on reverse (4510A, 4511A, 4512A, 4513A, 4514A, 4515) (Issued: 2,000)......................	(6)	225
PBS10–**2008**	Britannia proofs, £2 – 20p (4506, 4516, 4525, 4535) (Issued: 2,500)	(4)	150
PBS11–**2009**	Britannia proofs, £2 – 20p (4501, 4517, 4526, 4536) (Issued: 2,500)	(4)	150
PBS12–**2010**	Britannia proofs, £2 – 20p (4502, 4518, 4527, 4537) (Edition: 3,500)............	(4)	150
PBS13–**2011**	Britannia proofs, £2 – 20p (4508, 4519, 4528, 45387) (Edition: 3,500).......	(4)	195
PBS14–**2012**	Britannia proofs, £2 – 20p, (As PB02) (Issued: 2,595)	(4)	195
PBS15–**2012**	Britannia £1 proofs, set of nine different reverse designs (4510 to 4514, and 4516 to 4519) (Issued: 1,656)........................	(9)	400
PBS16–**2013**	Britannia proofs, £2 – 10p, (0.999 silver) (4509,4560,4529,4539 and 4550) (Issued: 3,087)	(5)	450
PBS17–**2013**	Britannia proofs, 20p and 10p (0.999 silver) (4539 and 4550)......................	(2)	39
PBS18–**2014**	Britannia proofs, £2 – 5 pence, (0.999 silver) (5025, 4702, 5015, 4540, 4681 and 4675) (Edition: 1,750)................................	(6)	200
PBS19–**2014**	Britannia proofs, 20p – 5 pence, (0.999 silver) (Edition: 1,000)...................	(3)	45
PBS20–**2015**	Britannia proofs, £2 – 5 pence, (0.999 silver) (5026, 5020, 5016, 5010, 5005 and 5000) (Edition: 1,750)................................	(6)	200
PBS21–**2015**	Britannia proofs, 20p – 5 pence, (0.999 silver) (Edition: 1,000)...................	(3)	45
PBS22–**2016**	Britannia proofs, £2 – 5 pence, (0.999 silver) (Edition: 1,100)....................	(6)	200

Gold Sovereign Proof Sets   £

Many of the coins that appear in the Gold proof sets were also offered for sale as individual coins in presentation cases with appropriate certificates. There are collectors of particular denominations such as £2 pieces, sovereigns and half sovereigns who request coins as issued i.e. in their cases with certificates rather than buying coins taken from sets. As a consequence, many of these individual coins command a premium over those that might have come from cased sets. As a result the prices for sets are often less than the sum of the individual coins.

			£
PGS01–**1980**	Gold £5 to half-sovereign (4201, 4203-4205) (Issued: 10,000)......................	(4)	3000
PGS02–**1981**	U.K. Proof coin Commemorative collection. (Consists of £5, sovereign, 'Royal Wedding' Crown (4229) in silver, plus base metal proofs 50p to ½p), (Not known)	(9)	2200
PGS03–**1982**	Gold £5 to half-sovereign (as 1980 issue) (Issued: 2,500)............................	(4)	3450
PGS04–**1983**	Gold £2, sovereign and half-sovereign, (4203 – 4205) (Not known)	(3)	1150
PGS05–**1984**	Gold £5, sovereign and half-sovereign, (4201, 4204 and 4205) (Issued: 7,095)	(3)	2250
PGS06–**1985**	Gold £5 to half-sovereign (4251, 4261, 4271, 4276) (Issued: 5,849).............	(4)	2800
PGS07–**1986**	Gold Commonwealth games £2, sovereign and half-sovereign (4311, 4271 and 4276) (Issued: 12,500)................................	(3)	1150
PGS08–**1987**	Gold £2, sovereign and half-sovereign (4261, 4271 and 4276) (Issued: 12,500)	(3)	1150
PGS09–**1988**	Gold £2 to half-sovereign, (as 1987 issue) (Issued: 11,192)........................	(3)	1150
PGS10–**1989**	Sovereign Anniversary Gold £5 to half-sovereign (4254, 4263, 4272, 4277), (Issued: 5,000)................................	(4)	5250
PGS11–**1989**	Gold £2 to half-sovereign (4263, 4272 and 4277) (Issued: 7,936)	(3)	2800
PGS12–**1990**	Gold £5 to half-sovereign (as 1985 issue), (Issued: 1,721)...........................	(4)	2800
PGS13–**1990**	Gold £2 to half-sovereign (as 1988 issue), (Issued: 1,937)...........................	(3)	1150
PGS14–**1991**	Gold £5 to half-sovereign (as 1985 issue) (Issued: 1,336)...........................	(4)	2800
PGS15–**1991**	Gold £2 to half-sovereign (as 1987 issue (Issued: 1,152)............................	(3)	1150

£

PGS16–**1992**	Gold £5 to half-sovereign (as 1985 issue) (Issued: 1,165)	(4)	2800
PGS17–**1992**	Gold £2 to half-sovereign (as 1987 issue) (Issued: 967)	(3)	1150
PGS18–**1993**	Gold £5 to half-sovereign with silver Pistrucci medal in case (Issued: 1,078)	(5)	2800
PGS19–**1993**	Gold £2 to half-sovereign (as 1985 issue) (Issued: 663)	(3)	1150
PGS20–**1994**	Gold £5, £2, sovereign and half-sovereign (4251, 4314, 4271 and 4276) (Issued: 918)	(4)	2800
PGS21–**1994**	Gold £2, sovereign and half-sovereign (4314, 4271 and 4276) (Issued: 1,249)	(3)	1150
PGS22–**1995**	Gold £5,£2,sovereign and half-sovereign (4251,4315,4271and 4276) (Issued: 718)	(4)	2800
PGS23–**1995**	Gold £2, sovereign and half-sovereign (4315, 4271 and 4276) (Issued: 1,112)	(3)	1150
PGS24–**1996**	Gold £5 to half-sovereign (as 1985 issue) (Issued: 742)	(4)	2800
PGS25–**1996**	Gold £2 to half-sovereign (as 1987 issue) (Issued: 868)	(3)	1150
PGS26–**1997**	Gold £5,£2,sovereign and half-sovereign (4251,4318,4271 and 4276) (Issued: 860)	(4)	2800
PGS27–**1997**	Gold £2 to half-sovereign (4318, 4271 and 4276) (Issued: 817)	(3)	1150
PGS28–**1998**	Gold £5 to half sovereign (4400, 4420, 4430, 4440) (Issued: 789)	(4)	2800
PGS29–**1998**	Gold £2 to half sovereign (4420, 4430, 4440) (Issued: 560)	(3)	1150
PGS30–**1999**	Gold £5, £2, sovereign and half sovereign (4400, 4571, 4430 and 4440) (Issued: 991)	(4)	2800
PGS31–**1999**	Gold £2, sovereign and half sovereign (4571, 4430 and 4440) (Issued: 912)	(3)	1150
PGS32–**2000**	Gold £5 to half-sovereign (as 1998 issue) (Issued: 1,000)	(4)	2800
PGS33–**2000**	Gold £2 to half-sovereign (as 1998 issue) (Issued: 1,250)	(3)	1150
PGS34–**2001**	Gold £5,£2,sovereign and half sovereign (4400, 4572, 4430 and 4440) (Issued: 1,000)	(4)	2800
PGS35–**2001**	Gold £2 , sovereign and half sovereign (4572,4430 and 4440)(Issued: 891)	(3)	1150
PGS36–**2002**	Gold £5 to half sovereign (4401, 4421, 4431, 4441) (Issued: 3,000)	(4)	3300
PGS37–**2002**	Gold £2 to half sovereign (4421, 4431, 4441) (Issued: 3,947)	(3)	1150
PGS38–**2003**	Gold £5 to half sovereign (as 1998 issue) (Issued: 2,050)	(4)	2800
PGS39–**2003**	Gold £2, sovereign and half sovereign (4577, 4430 and 4440) (Issued: 1,737)	(3)	1150
PGS40–**2004**	Gold £5 to half sovereign (as 1998 issue) (Issued: 1,749)	(4)	2800
PGS41–**2004**	Gold £2, sovereign and half sovereign (4578, 4430 and 4440) (Issued: 761)	(3)	1150
PGS42–**2005**	Gold £5 to half sovereign (4402, 4422, 4432, 4442 (Issued: 2,161)	(4)	3250
PGS43–**2005**	Gold £2 to half sovereign (4422, 4432, 4442) (Issued: 797)	(3)	1450
PGS44–**2006**	Gold £5 to half sovereign (as 1998 issue) (Issued: 1,750)	(4)	2800
PGS45–**2006**	Gold £2 to half sovereign (as 1998 issue) (Issued: 540)	(3)	1150
PGS46–**2007**	Gold £5 to half sovereign (as 1998 issue) (Issued: 1,750)	(4)	2800
PGS47–**2007**	Gold £2 to half sovereign (as 1998 issue) (Issued: 651)	(3)	1150
PGS48–**2007**	Gold sovereign and half sovereign (4430 and 4440) (Issued: 818)	(2)	560
PGS49–**2008**	Gold £5 to half sovereign (as 1998 issue) (Issued: 1,750)	(4)	2800
PGS50–**2008**	Gold £2 to half sovereign (as 1998 issue) (Issued: 583)	(3)	1150
PGS51–**2008**	Gold sovereign and half sovereign (as 2007 issue) (Issued: 804, in addition to individual coin issues)	(2)	560
PGS52–**2009**	Gold £5, £2, sovereign, half sovereign, and quarter sovereign (4403, 4423, 4433, 4443, and 4445) (Issued: 1,750)	(5)	2800
PGS53–**2009**	Gold £2, sovereign and half sovereign (4423, 4433 and 4445) (Edition: 750)	(3)	1150
PGS54–**2009**	Gold sovereign and half sovereign (4433 and 4443) (Edition: 1,000)	(2)	560
PGS55–**2010**	Gold £5 to quarter sovereign (as 2009 issue) (Edition: 1,750)	(5)	2800
PGS56–**2010**	Gold £2 to half sovereign (as 2009 issue) (Edition: 750)	(3)	1150
PGS57–**2010**	Gold sovereign, half sovereign and quarter sovereign (4433, 4443 and 4445) (Edition: 1,500)	(3)	675
PGS58–**2011**	Gold £5 to quarter sovereign (as 2010 issue) (Edition: 1,500)	(5)	2800
PGS59–**2011**	Gold £2 to quarter sovereign (4423, 4433, 4443 and 4445) (Edition: 200)	(4)	1275
PGS60–**2011**	(Previously listed as PGS59) Gold £2 to half sovereign (as 2010 issue) (Edition: 750)	(3)	1200

£

PGS61–**2011**	(Previously listed as PGS60) Gold sovereign, half sovereign and quarter sovereign (4433, 4443 and 4445) (Edition: 1,000)	(3)	675
PGS62–**2012**	Gold £5, £2, sovereign, half sovereign and quarter sovereign (4404, 4424, 4434, 4444 and 4446) (Issued: 956)	(5)	4250
PGS63–**2012**	Gold £2 to quarter sovereign (4424, 4434, 4444 and 4446) (Edition: 159)	(4)	1800
PGS64–**2012**	Gold £2 to half sovereign (4424, 4434 and 4444) (Issued: 335)	(3)	1650
PGS65–**2012**	Gold sovereign, half sovereign and quarter sovereign (4433, 4443 and 4445) (Issued: 701)	(3)	1000
PGS66–**2012**	BU Gold £2 to half sovereign (4424, 4434 and 4444) (Edition: 60)	(3)	2000
PGS67–**2013**	Gold £5, £2, sovereign, half sovereign and quarter sovereign (4403, 4423, 4433, 4443 and 4445) (Issued: 388)	(5)	2800
PGS68–**2013**	Gold £2 to half sovereign (4423, 4433 and 4445) (Issued: 380)	(3)	1150
PGS69–**2013**	Gold sovereign, half sovereign and quarter sovereign (4433, 4443 and 4445) (Issued: 652)	(3)	675
PGS70–**2013**	BU Gold £2 to half sovereign (4424, 4434 and 4444) (Issued: 124)	(3)	1750
PGS71–**2014**	Gold £5, £2, sovereign, half sovereign and quarter sovereign (4403, 4423, 4433, 4443 and 4445) (Edition: 750)	(5)	2800
PGS72–**2014**	Gold £2 to half sovereign (4423, 4433 and 4445) (Edition: 500)	(3)	1150
PGS73–**2014**	Gold sovereign, half sovereign and quarter sovereign (4433, 4443 and 4445) (Edition: 750)	(3)	675
PGS73–**2015**	Gold £5, £2, sovereign, half sovereign and quarter sovereign (4403, 4423, 4433, 4443 and 4445) (Edition: 500)	(5)	2800
PGS74–**2015**	Gold £2 to half sovereign (4423, 4433 and 4445) (Edition: 500)	(3)	1200
PGS75–**2015**	Gold sovereign, half sovereign and quarter sovereign (4433, 4443 and 4445) (Edition: 1,000)	(3)	675
PGS76–**2015**	New obverse portrait Gold £5, £2, sovereign, half sovereign and quarter sovereign (4411, 4425, 4435, 4415 and 4447) (Edition: 350)	(5)	4250
PGS77–**2015**	New obverse portrait Gold £2 to half sovereign (4425, 4435 and 4415) (Edition:500)	(3)	1750
PGS78–**2016**	New obverse portrait Gold £5 to quarter sovereign (Edition: 500	(5)	4300
PGS79–**2016**	New obverse portrait Gold £2 to half sovereign (4425, 4435 and 4415) (Edition: 350)	(3)	1600
PGS80–**2016**	New obverse portrait Gold sovereign, half sovereign and quarter sovereign (4433, 4443 and 4445) (Edition: 750)	(3)	900
PGS81–**2017**	New obverse layout and reverse Gold £5 to quarter sovereign (Edition: 750)	(5)	3300
PGS82–**2017**	New obverse layout and reverse Gold £2 to half sovereign (4425, 4435 and 4415) (Edition: 450)	(3)	1450
PGS83–**2017**	New obverse layout and reverse Gold sovereign, half sovereign and quarter sovereign (4433, 4443 and 4445) (Edition: 1000)	(3)	750

Britannia Gold Proof Sets   £

PBG01–**1987**	Britannia Proofs £100, £50, £25, £10 (4281, 4286, 4291, and 4296), alloyed with copper (Issued: 10,000)	(4)	2300
PBG02–**1987**	Britannia Proofs £25, £10 (4291 and 4296) (Issued: 11,100)	(2)	450
PBG03–**1988**	Britannia Proofs £100–£10 (as 1987 issue) (Issued: 3,505)	(4)	2300
PBG04–**1988**	Britannia Proofs £25, £10 (as 1987 issue) (Issued: 894)	(2)	450
PBG05–**1989**	Britannia Proofs £100–£10 (as 1987) (Issued: 2,268)	(4)	2300
PBG06–**1989**	Britannia Proofs £25, £10 (as 1987 issue) (Issued: 451)	(2)	450

£

PBG07–**1990**	Britannia Proofs, £100–£10, gold with the addition of silver alloy (4282, 4287, 4292, 4297) (Issued: 527)	(4)	2300

£

PBG08–**1991**	Britannia Proofs, as PBS07 (Issued: 509)	(4)	2300
PBG09–**1992**	Britannia Proofs, as PBS07 (Issued: 500)	(4)	2300
PBG10–**1993**	Britannia Proofs, as PBS07 (Issued: 462)	(4)	2300
PBG11–**1994**	Britannia Proofs, as PBS07 ((Issued: 435)	(4)	2300
PBG12–**1995**	Britannia Proofs, as PBS07 (Issued: 500)	(4)	2300
PBG13–**1996**	Britannia Proofs, as PBS07 (Issued: 483)	(4)	2300
PBG14–**1997**	Britannia proofs £100, £50, £25, £10 (4283, 4288, 4293, 4298) (Issued: 892)	(4)	2850
PBG15–**1998**	Britannia proofs £100, £50, £25, £10 (4450, 4460, 4470, 4480) (Issued: 750)	(4)	2300
PBG16–**1999**	Britannia Proofs, as PBS15 (Issued: 740)	(4)	2300
PBG17–**2000**	Britannia Proofs, as PBS15 (Issued: 750)	(4)	2300
PBG18–**2001**	Britannia Proofs £100, £50, £25, £10 (4451, 4461, 4471, 4481) (Issued: 1,000)	(4)	2550
PBG19–**2002**	Britannia Proofs, as PBS15 (Issued: 945)	(4)	2300
PBG20–**2003**	Britannia Proofs £100, £50, £25, £10 (4452, 4462, 4472, 4482) (Issued: 1,250)	(4)	2500
PBG21–**2003**	Britannia Proofs £50, £25, £10 (4462, 4472, 4482) (Issued: 825)	(3)	1150
PBG22–**MD**	Britannia BU £100 set of four different designs, 1987, 1997, 2001, 2003 (4281, 4283, 4451, 4452) (Edition: 2,500)	(4)	5000
PBG23–**2004**	Britannia Proofs, as PBS15 (Issued: 973)	(4)	2300
PBG24–**2004**	Britannia Proofs, £50, £25, £10 (4460, 4470, 4480) (Issued: 223)	(3)	1100
PBG25–**2005**	Britannia Proofs, £100, £50, £25, £10 (4453, 4463, 4473, 4483) (Issued: 1,439)	(4)	2300
PBG26–**2005**	Britannia Proofs, £50, £25, £10 (4463, 4473, 4483) (Issued: 417)	(3)	1100
PBG27–**2006**	Britannia Proofs, as PBS15 (Issued: 1,163)	(4)	2300
PBG28–**2006**	Britannia set of five different proof £25 designs (4470, 4471, 4472, 4473, 4474) (Edition: 250)	(5)	1650
PBG29–**2007**	(Previously listed as **PBS28**) Britannia Proofs, £100, £50, £25, £10 (4454, 4464, 4475, 4484) (Issued: 1,250)	(4)	2300
PBG30–**2008**	Britannia Proofs, £100, £50, £25, £10 (4455, 4465, 4476, 4485) (Issued: 1,250)	(4)	2300
PBG31–**2009**	Britannia Proofs, £100, £50, £25, £10 (4456, 4466, 4474, 4486) (Edition: 1,250)	(4)	2300
PBG32–**2010**	Britannia Proofs, £100, £50, £25, £10 (4457, 4467, 4477, 4487) (Issued: 1,250)	(4)	2300
PBG33–**2010**	Britannia Proofs, £50, £25, £10 (4467, 4475, 4487) (Edition: 500)	(3)	1100
PBG34–**2011**	Britannia Proofs, £100, £50, £25, £10 (4458, 4468, 4478, 4488) (Edition: 1,000)	(4)	2500
PBG35–**2011**	Britannia Proofs, £50, £25, £10 (4468, 4478, 4488) (Edition: 250)	(3)	1200
PBG36–**2012**	Britannia Proofs, as PBS15 (Issued: 352)	(4)	2300
PBG37–**2012**	Britannia Proofs, £50, £25 and £10 (4460, 4470 and 4480) (Issued: 99)	(3)	1100
PBG38–**MD**	Britannia Proof set of 1987 (£100 to £10, struck in copper alloyed gold, see PBS01), and set of 2012 (£100 to £10, struck in silver alloyed gold, see PBS36) (Issued: 13, sets of 1987 from the secondary market)	(8)	4600
PBG39–**2013**	Britannia Proofs, £100 - £1, (0.9999 gold), (4459, 4469, 4479, 4489 and 4760) (Issued: 261)	(5)	2750
PBG40–**2013**	Britannia Proofs, Premium set, £50, £25 and £10, (0.9999 gold), (4469, 4479 and 4489) (Issued: 90)	(3)	1100
PBG41–**2013**	Britannia Proofs, £25, £10 and £1, (0.9999 gold), (4479, 4489 and 4760) (Issued 136)	(3)	525
PBG42–**2014**	Britannia Proofs, £100 – 50 pence, (0.9999 gold), (5055, 5050, 5045, 4490, 4776 and 4740) (Edition: 250)	(6)	2600
PGB43–**2014**	Britannia Proofs, £50 – £10, (0.9999 gold) (Edition: 100)	(3)	1175
PGB44–**2014**	Britannia Proofs, £25 – £1, (0.9999 gold) (Edition: 150)	(3)	525
PBG45–**2015**	Britannia Proofs, £100 - £1, (0.9999 gold), (5056, 5051, 5046, 5040, 5035 and 5030) (Edition: 250)	(6)	2600
PGB46–**2015**	Britannia Proofs, £50 – £10, (0.9999 gold), (Edition: 100)	(3)	1175
PGB47–**2015**	Britannia Proofs, £10 – 50 pence, (0.9999 gold) (Edition: 250)	(3)	275

Gold Coin Proof Sets £

PCGS1–**2002**	Commonwealth Games 'Bimetallic' £2 (4573, 4574, 4575 and 4576) in gold (Issued: 315).....................	(4)	2400
PGJS1–**2002**	'Golden Jubilee' £5, 'Bimetallic' £2, 'English' £1, 50p to 1p and Maundy coins, 4p-1p, in gold proof (4555, 4570, 4594, 4610, 4630, 4650, 4670, 4212-4215) (Issued: 2,002).....................	(13)	5250
PGBNS–**2006**	'Bimetallic' 'Isambard Brunel' £2 (4581) and 'Bimetallic' 'Paddington Station' £2 (4582) gold proofs (Edition: taken from individual coin limits)	(2)	1200
PGVCS–**2006**	'Victoria Cross' 50 pence (4617), 'Wounded Colleague' 50 pence (4618) gold proof (Edition: taken from individual coin limits)....................	(2)	1200
PGBS1–**MD**	Set of four £1 coins 'Forth Rail Bridge' (4595), 'Menai Straits Bridge' (4596) 'MacNiell's Egyptian Arch' (4597) and 'Gateshead Millennium Bridge' (4598) in gold proof (Edition: 300 sets taken from individual coin limits)...........	(4)	2800
PGEBCS–**2008**	'Emblems of Britain', 'UK' £1 (4590), 'Britannia' 50 pence (4610), 20 pence to 1p gold proofs (Issued: 708).........................	(7)	3100
PGRSAS–**2008**	'The Royal Shield of Arms', 'Royal Shield' £1 (4604) to 1p gold proof (4611, 4631, 4651, 4671, 4691, and 4711) (Issued: 886)	(7)	3100
PG1PCS–**2008**	Set of 14 different £1 reverse designs (4590 to 4603) (Issued: 150)...........	(14)	10000
PG50PCS–**2009**	Set of sixteen 50 pence reverse designs marking 40th Anniversary of the introduction of the 50 pence denomination (4610- 4625) gold proofs (Edition: 125).....................	(16)	9000
PG50PPCS–**2009**	Set of sixteen 50 pence reverse designs marking 40th Anniversary of the introduction of the 50 pence denomination (4610- 4625) gold proof piedfort (Edition: 40)	(16)	20000
PGDJS–**2012**	Diamond Jubilee £5, (4569), 'Bimetallic' 'Charles Dickens' £2 (4730), 'Bimetallic' £2 (4570) 'Royal Shield' £1(4604), 50 pence to 1 pence (4620, 4631, 4652, 4672, 4691 and 4711) gold proofs (Edition: 150)...................	(10)	6000
PGCS–**2012**	Diamond Jubilee £5, (4569) and Golden Jubilee £5, (4555) (Edition: 60)..	(2)	3250
PGCS2–**2012**	Diamond Jubilee £5, (4569) and £2 (Sovereign design, 4424) set of two (Edition : 60, taken from individual coins limits)........................	(2)	2600
PGCS3–**MD**	Set of six £2 with Sporting connections, Commonwealth Games 1986 (4311), European Football Championship 1996 (4317) and Commonwealth Games 2002 (4573 to 4576) coins obtained from the secondary market (Edition: 50)........................	(6)	3600
PGCAS–**2013**	'Coronation' £5, (4751), 'Bimetallic' 'Guinea' £2 (4731) 'Bimetallic' 'Roundel' £2 (4732), 'Bimetallic' 'Train' £2 (4733), 'Bimetallic' £2 (4570) 'Royal Shield' £1 (4604), 'England' £1 (4720), 'Wales' £1 (4721), 50 pence 'Ironside' (4628), 50 pence to 1 pence (4620, 4631, 4652, 4672, 4691 and 4711) gold proofs (Issued: 59)........................	(15)	10000
PGLUS–**2013**	Bimetallic' 'Roundel' £2 (4732) and 'Bimetallic' 'Train' £2 (4733) gold proofs (Issued: 111)	(2)	1500
PGQPS–**2013**	Queen's Portrait set of £5 coins, (4754 – 4757) gold proofs (Issued: 148).	(4)	8000
PG31S–**2013**	Thirtieth Anniversary set of three £1 coins, (4590, 4334 and 4604) gold proofs (Issued: 17)........................	(3)	3000
PGC14–**2014**	'Queen Anne' £5, (4758), 'Bimetallic' 'Trinity House' £2 (4734), 'Bimetallic' 'World War I' £2 (4735), 'Bimetallic' £2 (4570) 'Royal Shield' £1 (4604), 'Northern Ireland' £1 (4722), 'Scotland' £1 (4723.), and 50 pence 'Commonwealth Games' (4630), gold proofs (Edition:)........................	(6)	7000
PGC4P–**2015**	Fourth Portrait 'Bimetallic' £2 (4570) 'Royal Shield', £1 (4604), 50 pence to 1 pence (4620, 4636, 4652, 4672, 4691 and 4711), gold proofs, (Edition: 500)........................	(8)	3800
PGC5P–**2015**	Fifth Portrait 'Bimetallic' £2 (4736) 'Royal Shield', £1 (4604), 50 pence to 1 pence (4632, 4636, 4652, 4672, 4691 and 4711), gold proofs, (Edition: 500)........................	(8)	3800

£

PGC15–**2015**	Churchill £5, (4764), Waterloo £5, (4765) 'Bimetallic' 'Magna Carta' £2 (4737), 'Bimetallic' 'Royal Navy' £2 (4738), 50 pence 'Battle of Britain' (4632), gold proofs (Edition: 100)	(5)	5800
PGC16–**2014**	World War 1. Set of six £5, Renumbered (4850 – 4855), gold proofs (Edition: 20)	(6)	9999
PGC17–**2015**	World War 1. Second Set of six £5, (4856 – 4861), gold proofs (Edition: 25)	(6)	9999
PGC18–**2016**	Commemorative Proof set, Queen's Birthday £5, (4764), 'Bimetallic' £2 'Comedy', 'Bimetallic' £2 'History' (4738), 'Bimetallic' £2 'Tragedy' (4570), 'Bimetallic' £2 'The Army', 'Bimetallic' £2 'Great Fire', Royal Arms £1, 50 pence 'Battle of Hastings' (4632) gold proofs (Edition: 150).	(8)	6300
PGC19–**2016**	World War I. Third Set of six £5, gold proofs (Edition: 25)	(6)	10500

Platinum Coin Proof sets   £

PPBCS1–**2007**	Britannia Proofs £100, £50, £25, £10 (4454A, 4464A, 4474A and 4484A) (Issued: 250)	(4)	2800
PPBCS2–**2008**	Britannia Proofs £100, £50, £25, £10 (4455A, 4465, 4476A, and 4485A) (Edition: 250)	(4)	2800
PPEBCS–**2008**	'Emblems of Britain', 'UK' £1 (4590), 'Britannia' 50 pence (4610) and 20 pence to 1p (Issued: 250)	(7)	3500
PPRSAS–**2008**	'The Royal Shield of Arms', 'Royal Shield' £1 (4604) to 1p (4611, 4631, 4651, 4671, 4691, 4711) (Issued: 184)	(7)	3500

Pattern Proof sets   £

PPS1–**2003**	Silver proof set of £1 designs with plain edge and hallmark (4595A, 4596A, 4597A, 4598A) (Edition: 7,500)	(4)	75
PPS2–**2003**	Gold proof set of £1 designs with plain edge and hallmark (4595A, 4596A, 4597A, 4598A) (Edition: 3,000)	(4)	2300
PPS3–**2004**	Silver proof set of £1 designs with plain edge and hallmark (4595B, 4596B, 4597B, 4598B) (Edition: 5,000)	(4)	75
PPS4–**2004**	Gold proof set of £1 designs with plain edge and hallmark (4595B, 4596B, 4597B, 4598B) (Edition: 2,250)	(4)	2300

LONDON 2012 OLYMPIC AND PARALYMPIC GAMES

OCNS1–**MD**	Set of 29 50 pence coins in individual card packs (4960 to 4988)	(29)	90
OCNS2	Gold Medal Winners set of 50 pence Cuni and £5 Olympic 2012 £5, (Athletics, 4960, Boxing, 4967, Canoeing, 4968, Cycling, 4961, Equestrian, 4969, Rowing, 4978, Sailing, 4979, Shooting, 4980, Taekwondo, 4982, Tennis, 4983, Triathlon, 4984 and £5, 4924) (Edition: 2,012)	(12)	45
OCNS3	Five pounds.(crowns). Set of the four Countdown issues and the Official Olympic and Paralympic £5 cuni coins. (4920 to 4925). (Edition: 2,012)	(6)	70
OCNS4	Five pounds. (crowns). Set of four Countdown issues (4920 – 4923)	(4)	45

Silver coin sets   £

OSS1–**2009**.	The Mind of Britain. Set of six £5 silver proofs (4930, 4931, 4932, 4933, 4934 and 4935) (Edition: each coin 95,000)	(6)	300
OSS2–**2010**	The Body of Britain. Set of six £5 silver proofs (4936, 4937, 4938, 4939, 4940 and 4941) (Edition: each coin 95,000)	(6)	300

£

OSS3–**2010**	The Spirit of Britain. Set of six £5 silver proofs (4942, 4943, 4944, 4945, 4946 and 4947) (Edition: each coin 95,000)	(6)	300
OSS4–**MD**	Great British Icons. Set of 6 £5 silver proofs (4930,4931,4938,4944,4945, 4946) (Edition: 10,000 taken from individual coin limits of 95,000)	(6)	550
OSS5–**MD**	The Mind, Body and Spirit of Britain. Set of 18 £5 silver proofs (4930 to 4947)	(18)	1650
OSS6–**2011**	Set of 29 50 pence silver brilliant uncirculated coins (4960 to 4988)	(29)	900
OSS7–**2011**	Gold Medal Winners set of 50 pence silver brilliant uncirculated coins and £5 Olympic 2012 silver proof, (Athletics, 4960, Boxing, 4967, Canoeing, 4968, Cycling, 4961, Equestrian, 4969, Rowing, 4978, Sailing, 4979, Shooting, 4980, Taekwondo, 4982, Tennis, 4983, Triathlon, 4984 and £5, 4924), (Edition: 999 but coins taken from individual issue limits)	(12)	550
OSS8–**2011**	Accuracy. Set of six 50 pence silver brilliant uncirculated coins depicting various sports (Badminton, 4964, Basketball, 4965, Fencing, 4970, Football, 4971, Hockey, 4975, and Tennis, 4983) (Edition: 2,012 but taken from individual issue limits)	(6)	280
OSS9–**2011**	Agility. Set of six 50 pence silver brilliant uncirculated coins depicting various sports (Boxing, 4967, Equestrian, 4969, Gymnastics, 4973, Judo, 4976, Sailing, 4979, and Taekwondo, 4982) (Edition: 2,012 but taken from individual issue limits)	(6)	280
OSS10–**2011**	Speed. Set of six 50 pence silver brilliant uncirculated coins depicting various sports (Athletics, 4960, Aquatics, 4962, Canoeing, 4968, Cycling, 4961, Rowing, 4978, Triathlon, 4984) (Edition: 2,012 but taken from individual issue limits)	(6)	280
OSS11–**MD**	Five pounds.(crowns). Set of the four Countdown issues and the Official Olympic and Paralympic £5 proof silver coins. (4920 to 4925). (Edition: 800 taken from individual issue limits)	(6)	500

Gold coin sets.

£

OGS1–**2008**	**(Previously listed as PG2PCS).** 'Bimetallic' 'Centenary of Olympic Games of 1908' £2 (4585) and 'Bimetallic' 'United Kingdom Olympic Handover Ceremony' £2 (4951) gold proofs (Edition: 250)	(2)	1200
OGS2–**2010**	'Faster' 2-coin proof set, two £25, (4905 and 4906) (Edition: taken from individual coin Limits)	(2)	800
OGS3–**2010**	'Faster' 3-coin proof set, £100, and two £25, (4915, 4905 and 4906) (Edition: 4,000)	(3)	2400
OGS4–**2011**	'Higher' 2-coin proof set, two £25, (4907 and 4908) (Edition: taken from individual coin limits)	(2)	800
OGS5–**2011**	'Higher' 3-coin proof set, £100, and two £25, (4916, 4907 and 4908) (Edition: 4,000)	(3)	2400
OGS6–**2012**	'Stronger' 2-coin proof set, two £25, (4909 and 4910) (Edition: taken from individual coin limits)	(2)	800
OGS7–**2012**	'Stronger' 3-coin proof set, £100, and two £25, (4917, 4909 and 4910) (Edition: 4,000)	(3)	2400
OGS8–**MD**	'Faster', 'Higher' and 'Stronger' set of three £100 (4915 – 4917) and six £25 (4905 – 4910) (Edition: 1,000 taken from individual coin limits)	(9)	8000
OGS9–**MD**	'Countdown to London' set of four £5 gold proof coins (4920 – 4923)	(4)	8000
OGS10–**2012**	Set of £5 proof London Olympic Games and Paralympic Games (4924 and 4925) (Edition: taken from individual coin limits)	(2)	4000